TAXIDERMY

TAXIDERMY

a complete manual

John C. Metcalf
FZS, MBOU

cut neck here

Duckworth

Second impression 1987
First published in 1981 by
Gerald Duckworth & Co. Ltd.,
The Old Piano Factory,
43 Gloucester Crescent, London N.W.1

ISBN 0 7156 1051 1 cased
ISBN 0 7156 1565 3 paper

British Library Cataloguing in Publication Data

Metcalf, John C
 Taxidermy.
 1. Taxidermy
 I. Title
 579'.4 QL63

 ISBN 0-7156-1051-1
 ISBN 0-7156-1565-3 Pbk

Photoset in Great Britain by
The Allen Lithographic Company Limited
Kirkcaldy
and printed by
Unwin Brothers Limited
Old Woking

Contents

Plates

(between pp. 88 and 89)

Preface

Taxidermy, like so many of the 'old crafts', has had a varied history. Early exponents of the art, such as Charles Waterton, pioneered many techniques in keeping with the times. Each man kept his own secrets, and practitioners were few and far between. In Victorian times, however, the tradition of taxidermy prospered. No 'civilised' household was complete without its quota of curios, and fashion decreed a case or two of mixed birds or a tea-party of kittens. Every town and city boasted at least two or three taxidermists, and every pampered pet was preserved for posterity. The demand was such that the taxidermist would spend a good deal of his time in the field, shooting and trapping anything that came his way. Birds of prey were very popular, as were colourful birds, but even common birds had their uses – if you shot enough you were sure to find a freak, and normal birds could always be used to make up a tableau for 'Who Killed Cock Robin'. Nor did mammals escape the slaughter. Red squirrels are pretty little animals and by a little anthropomorphic manipulation could be turned into boxers, country gentlemen or a ladies' sewing circle.

Modern taxidermy embraces many more distinct techniques in this age of plastics, polyvinyl chlorides and the method of dehydration from the frozen state known as 'freeze-drying'. These aids, however, were not available to help the old masters with the art of taxidermy.

This book is designed to bring together the various methods of taxidermy, old and new. Although we have made a technical step forward, the craft of taxidermy still calls for much skill, requiring technical and artistic ability, experience and a considerable knowledge of birds and mammals in life. These elements are essential if the specimens are to be mounted in lifelike postures. One cannot master the art of taxidermy without practising on a large number of specimens. Nowadays there are many obstacles in the way of obtaining material. The various acts and laws relating to wildlife, quite rightly, prohibit the shooting or trapping of most birds and mammals. There are many pressures on our wildlife: crop sprays, destruction of habitat, disturbance by humans, new methods of farming, pollution, all of which are reducing the wildlife population. Anyone who, to further his taxidermy, whether as a hobby or a business, begins shooting or trapping is doing great harm, as well as breaking the law. Fortunately, however, there is one large and often overlooked source of material. Many birds and mammals are killed daily on our roads, and these corpses are often suitable for taxidermy and can supply most of your needs. An alternative source is the local fishmonger and poulterer. By taking care in the selection of the specimens, you can obtain, in season, pheasants, partridge, grouse, duck, plovers, capercaillie and ptarmigan as well as rabbits and hares. You can double your pleasure, for you can both practise taxidermy and eat well.

A world-wide interest in taxidermy has produced very high standards of work in both Europe and America. This book originates in Britain. American readers should realise that certain materials that we use have slightly different names. Thus 'cotton-wool' is cotton batting, and 'wood-wool' excelsior; 'tow' is a produce from the jute plant. I also refer to 'cotton', which is simply household sewing thread and is easily obtained. By pulling this thread through a small block of wax it can be made stronger and waterproof. Chemicals can be bought from the 'chemist' (or drug store) and tools from the 'ironmonger' (or hardware store).

Thanks are due to the following who have helped me with the preparation of this book: Mr W. H. Barrow, Bristol City Museum, England, Dr D. Burkel, Dr J. E. Cooper, Mr P. Condor, Miss J. Coy, Mr D. Foxwell, Mr A. Gordon, Mr R. H. Harris, Mr S. R. Hedges, Mr A. D. Irvin, Mr N. Killips, Dr J. H. Matthias, Mr J. McGibbon, Mr C. E. Owen, Mrs S. J. Patrick, Mr P. Robinson, Mr D. P. Sharp, Mrs C. Thawley, Mr J. G. Williams, Mr M. B. Withers. Special thanks go to my wife whose time and patience have helped greatly in producing the manuscript.

J.C.M.

1

An Historical Perspective

The word 'taxidermy' is derived from the Greek *taxis* meaning 'fixing' or 'arrangement', and *derma* meaning 'skin'. Taking this 'skin fixing' as a literal definition, it is clear that the origins of taxidermy must go back to the emergence of the civilising influences in man himself. Man was a hunter and scavenger long before he farmed the land, and the use of animal hide for clothing must have involved some basic means of preservation – even if it was no more than careful fat removal and drying of the hide. 'Skin fixing' must have been a widely practised skill and one of vital importance in the temperate regions of the world where cold winters make warm clothing essential.

With the flowering of the Near Eastern civilisations, and the dominance of the Egyptians and their religion in the Nile Valley, the practice of embalming – preserving bodies from decay by use of aromatics, antiseptics and desiccation – grew and was perfected until it became an art form. Corpses were disembowelled, treated with preservatives, dried, bound and laid in a tomb with everyday articles which the subject could use in the next life. The idea behind such ritualised embalming was not to preserve an attractive, lifelike form but rather to prevent the body from decaying. It could then be repossessed by the spirit on completing the cycle of re-incarnation. The embalming techniques were remarkably successful, as witnessed by the number of perfectly preserved mummies in museums today.

Many animals have also been found in these tombs, preserved, again not for aesthetic considerations, but as a practical means of maintaining the bodies free from decay to await the return of their spirit, Master and animals could then live in the afterworld as they did before death on earth. Dogs, cats, apes, crocodiles, birds, sheep and oxen have all been found mummified in this way.

The aesthetics of embalming and mummification were directed to ends different from those of modern taxidermy. In mummification, emphasis was placed on the decoration of the tomb and sarcophagus rather than of the body itself. On the other hand, taxidermy is an attempt to give shape, attitude, and expression to the bodies of its subjects in order to make them appear as they did in life.

The beginnings of true taxidermy, as opposed to straightforward preservation, lie in sixteenth-century Holland. A Dutch nobleman collected a large number of tropical birds which he kept in a heated aviary. One night the birds were killed by fumes escaping from the heating furnace, and in his reluctance to dispose of the dead birds he sought advice on preservation from his country's most eminent chemists. They advised him to skin the birds and preserve the skins by filling them with 'spices from the Indies'. By the use of wires, much as is done today, he mounted the preserved skins on perches in a rough facsimile of life. He pursued his new hobby for many years and accumulated the first recorded systematic collection of mounted birds.

Taxidermy was performed with varying degrees of experimentation and success, and with a growing popularity throughout the seventeenth century. By the early eighteenth century some methods of preservation had achieved widespread acceptance and began to be published. In 1748-9, a Frenchman, Réaumur, a bird collector, published a memoir in the form of instructions to field collectors, on a

9

method of preserving bird skins for transportation. It involved saturating the dead birds in spirits of wine, which preserved them sufficiently until taxidermy could be carried out on them in Paris. On his death, the impressive cabinet of preserved birds which Réaumur collected was donated to the Museum of Paris and formed the early nucleus of its natural history collection.

In 1752, M. B. Stollas, another Parisian, went further than Réaumur in publishing a book entitled *Instructions on the Manner of Preparing Objects of Natural History*, which illustrated a number of ingenious methods of mounting birds and mammals, as well as giving recipes for preservation. E. F. Turgot appears to be the author of an anonymous work on taxidermy which was issued in Lyons around 1758. This illustrated work described various methods of skinning and mounting small birds and mammals. These techniques are sound but primitive, unlike the instructions in the same work for mounting reptiles, amphibians, fish and crustaceans, which are comparable with some present-day methods.

1786 saw the publication, again in France, of a work entitled *Treatise on the Manner of Stuffing and Preserving Animals and Skins* by the Abbé Manesse, which was presented to the Academy of Sciences in Paris. This book gives a number of useful practical hints for mounting birds, but falls down badly in its recommendations of preservatives. Alkali substitutes are preferred to the more usual poisons, and these are, at best, only effective in the short term and are never used today.

Later in the eighteenth century several German preparators published books on taxidermy. Bécoeur was particularly productive. He first developed arsenical soap, which was widely used as a preservative and is still in use today. He was also probably the first person to mount birds and mammals by replacing the cleaned and preserved skeleton inside the skin and filling it out with flax and cotton-wool. Again, he supported the models with wire, passing it along the vertebral column and along limb bones, so giving the mounts a degree of rigidity.

In 1855 J. S. Wiley published a pamphlet in Germany called 'Preparation and Preservation of Objects of Natural History', one of the more informative works of the period. This was soon followed by a three-volume work *The Manner of Collecting and Preparing Fishes and Reptiles* by another German preparator, W. Shilling.

Of the few American books to appear on taxidermy during the nineteenth century, Maynard's *Taxidermist's Guide* and *Taxidermist's Manual*, and also J. H. Batty's *Practical Taxidermy* should be noted.

For several years, the distinguished naturalist Prince Maximilian of Nieu Wied, Germany, explored various regions of North and South America, collecting specimens of birds and mammals, many of which can be seen today in the Museum of Natural History in New York. An early British taxidermist, Ogden, emigrated to America in 1840 and joined the Boston Museum at Tremont Temple, under the direction of the Boston Society of Natural History, where his work on large mammals, birds and reptiles gained a considerable reputation.

One of the most famous taxidermy businesses was founded in London in 1820 by Henry Ward, an eminent Victorian naturalist and taxidermist, who travelled the world with John James Audubon, perhaps the best-known American naturalist, and produced some of the most skilful and sought-after examples of the taxidermist's art. The business 'Wards of London' was continued by Henry Ward's sons, Edwin and Rowland. Work from these studios can still be seen in many museum collections, their reputation being based mainly on superlative modelling of birds and large mammals.

Another outstanding taxidermist working in the early part of the nineteenth century in England was Peter Spicer of Leamington Spa, whose specialities were game heads and bird modelling. He is said to have been taxidermist, by special warrant, to His Imperial Majesty the King of Spain. Among Spicer's patrons were the Duke of Cambridge, the Rt Hon. Countess of Harewood and the famous artist J. G. Millais, FZS.

During the nineteenth and the early twentieth century, taxidermy as a hobby and a profession began to establish itself in England. The number of taxidermists capable of producing fine work grew. Among these were James Gardner who held a royal warrant to Queen Victoria and preserved exotic foreign birds. His business was based in Oxford Street in London and his work can be seen in the Bognor Regis Museum in Sussex, the Curtis Museum in Alton, Hampshire and the Natural History Society Museum in Dorset. Leadbeater & Son, good taxidermists of their day, worked in London during the mid-nineteenth century. John Betteridge's business in Birmingham started in 1872 and was continued by his son, W. B. Betteridge, until 1951. Examples of their work can be seen in the Birmingham City Museum, the Herbert Museum and Art Gallery in Coventry, Leicester Museum and Art Gallery, and Sheffield City Museum. Montagu Browne ran a taxidermy business in Birmingham before becoming curator of Leicester Museum in 1881. Charles Kirk, the well-known taxidermist from Glasgow, was apprenticed to Rowland Ward of Ward's of London and set up his business in Glasgow around 1896. John Cullingford successfully preserved both birds and mammals at the University Museum in Durham between 1878 and 1905. Three other members of the Cullingford family also operated in Durham in the early twentieth century, and examples of their work can be seen in Leicester Museum, Hancock Museum in Newcastle-upon-Tyne and the Bognor Regis Museum. William Farren, a reputable taxidermist, worked from the late nineteenth century to the early twentieth. Edwin Hart of Christchurch, Hampshire was a naturalist and wildfowler. Between 1870 and 1900, he formed the very fine Hart Collection which consists of about 350 cased exhibits, most of which can be seen in the Leicester Museum. Thomas Edward Gunn & Son of Norwich were in the taxidermy business from around 1826 to 1942. They were a well-known firm whose fine work can be seen in the Booth Bird Museum in Brighton and also in the Ipswich and Leicester Museums and the Castle Museum in Norwich. At the International Fishes' Exhibition in London in 1883, Thomas Gunn was awarded a diploma of honour and gold and silver medals. Among his patrons were Lord William Percy and Sir Harper Vauncey Crew of Caulk Abbey, Derbyshire. George Lodge (1860–1953), better known for his exquisite bird paintings, studied taxidermy as a hobby and became a very capable preparator. Arthur Ponchard of Ringwood, Hampshire, prepared an excellent collection of warblers from 1900 to 1940, and these can be seen in the Halifax Museum in Yorkshire.

Ireland, too, has its memorable taxidermists, one of whom was Alfred Sheals who worked in Belfast from 1860 to 1890. Before the Second World War, Williams & Sons of Dublin produced very fine work. In 1946, one of the sons of this family, A. E. Williams, became taxidermist to Leicester Museum, specialising in bird mounting. He retired in 1971, and it was this position that I later filled.

Taxidermy, as we know it today, has been practised only for about 350 years. The oldest known specimen, prepared in the 1600s, is a rhinoceros which is in the Royal Museum of Vertebrates in Florence, Italy. The method of preparation is as yet undetermined. Many natural history museum collections began as donations of early preserved material, and these are the most appropriate institutions to approach for study of the oldest specimens. The British Museum in London is typical of many. The Sloan collection, donated to it in 1753, was one of the British Museum's earliest acquisitions, and specimens from it survive today. Commercial markets for mounted birds and mammals exist and it is still possible to obtain fine specimens mounted by famous names of the past at reasonable prices. But the growing popularity of taxidermy as a hobby and the limited supply of the earlier material means that prices are increasing.

Many collectors view their acquisitions as investments, in much the same way as any other collector of works of art, and this has the effect of pushing up the saleroom prices. Nevertheless, taxidermy for the enthusiast has its major rewards in personal achievement.

11

2

Health Hazards

Much of the material that the preparator will handle should be regarded as potentially dangerous. Specimens found dead by the general public and brought in by sportsmen and animals which have died in zoos are the main sources. Zoo animals are usually post-mortemed by the zoo veterinary surgeon before disposal. However, birds and mammals may come into your possession through animal importers or pet dealers. Most of this material will be found dead on arrival, or may well have died in transit and this can be the most hazardous source.

Exotic birds and animals which die on reaching, or shortly after reaching, their destinations have usually died as a result of stress, overcrowding, failure to acclimatise or similar factors..Some of these specimens may well have died from infectious diseases and unless a competent post-mortem is carried out the disease will go unrecognised. It is at this stage that the specimen is of great danger to those who come in contact with it.

PRECAUTIONS AGAINST DISEASE

The points previously mentioned are fairly general and apply to any establishment where disease risks might be incurred. However, some diseases are specific to museums. In most cases common sense should dictate the limits of practicability. Preparators, collectors and those who are in constant contact with specimens of natural history are at greatest risk. Persons from outside who handle and examine contaminated specimens also expose themselves to possible infection. Everyone involved in the handling of animal material should be made aware of the possible dangers and should observe simple hygiene precautions, such as washing and disinfecting hands after preparing material.

Over-clothing should be used, not only to protect personal clothing from stains but also so that it can be left in the studio after work. Rubber gloves should be used whenever possible. Paper face-masks should be used in some cases, e.g. when sawing bones. The mask will greatly reduce the amount of dust spores which could be inhaled or ingested.

Personnel should not smoke or eat while handling material so that infections cannot be transferred to the mouth and face. It is advisable for all preparators to be vaccinated against such diseases as tetanus. A BCG vaccination against tuberculosis is also advisable. Preparators should attend regularly at mass X-ray centres, in view of possible exposure to diseases affecting the chest, such as tuberculosis and histoplasmosis.

The following points should be considered in order to evaluate risks to human beings. Most infectious diseases are destroyed in various ways, e.g.:

(a) the passage of time
(b) desiccation
(c) daylight or rich ultra-violet light
(d) certain chemicals and disinfectants
(e) freezing and thawing repeatedly, although this is of little use to the preparator

It is interesting to note that the following methods may preserve the infectious agents:

(a) darkness
(b) protection by extraneous material
(c) refrigeration
(d) desiccation (some agents may be

preserved if rapidly desiccated or if protected by extraneous materials, e.g. mud, faeces or body tissue)

(e) freeze-drying is an efficient way of preserving these organisms, according to A.D. Irvin, J.E. Cooper and S.R. Hedges of the A.R.C. Institute for Research on Animal Diseases, Compton, Berkshire, England

I am extremely grateful to A.D. Irvin, J.E. Cooper and S.R. Hedges for allowing me to publish the list of bacterial, fungal, viral and rickettsial diseases (see Appendix 2).

RABIES

Rabies occurs in many parts of the world. However, it is still absent from Britain because of our island isolation, stringent legislation and other control measures.

There has been a considerable increase in wildlife rabies over the past decade which appears to be part of a cyclical pattern exhibited by this disease. According to the International Committee on Rabies in 1966, there was a similar worldwide epidemic about a hundred years ago. Wild animals are said to constitute the main reservoir of infection in many areas, and if this reservoir could be eliminated, the disease could probably be eradicated in those areas. Despite the increased knowledge of the epidemiology and method of control, the present outbreak appears to be on the increase as far as wildlife is concerned.

According to A.D. Irvin's *The Epidemiology of Wildlife Rabies*, of the nineteen orders of mammals only two, *Carnivora* and *Cheroptera*, are known to be reservoirs of rabies today. *Rodentia* may also be important in certain localised areas. Those commonly infected as incidental hosts are *Primates* (including man), *Artiodactyla* and *Perissodactyla*. Strict control measures are needed for pet monkeys, as they can present a serious hazard to human health. Many are not subjected to quarantine or any other form of clinical or laboratory examination. Other pets to be considered are carnivores, parrots, tortoises, terrapins and certain other reptiles.

In addition to its introduction through live animals, the possible presence of rabies in material sent to individuals and museums should also be considered. Much of this material is sent from abroad in the frozen state. Some smaller specimens, particularly bats, are freeze-dried. Both these methods favour the preservation of the rabies virus. Animals which have died in transit may be sent directly to museums, and a considerable health hazard is presented to the staff of these institutions.

Every person who is involved with taxidermy as a hobby or a profession should make himself aware of certain regulations regarding safety, first aid and cleanliness, and make every effort to abide by a code of conduct regarding personal hygiene and workshop cleanliness.

(a) Take great care if poisons are used; they should be stored properly and labelled.

(b) The taxidermist must be constantly aware of the dangers of poisons and where possible he must know the various antidotes, particularly in connection with the dangerous inhalation of solvents.

(c) Fire precautions must be observed. Inflammable liquids must be stored properly, and particular care must be taken against spontaneous combustion of wastes when using synthetic resins.

(d) Rubber gloves, face-masks and protective clothing should be worn where applicable.

(e) Accidents, no matter how slight, should be attended to immediately and a dressing applied. If a deep cut is inflicted, consult your doctor at once.

(f) Disease spreads, so every effort must be made to keep clean all instruments, working surfaces and workshop floors. Wash your hands frequently (see Appendix 2).

3

Tools and Materials

To attain the maximum success, the taxidermist must choose top quality tools. The materials must also be of good quality. First and foremost on the list of requirements is a workshop or working area, which must have:

(a) good lighting, both artificial and daylight
(b) good ventilation
(c) an easily cleaned working surface
(d) shelving to accommodate chemicals, preservatives, etc.
(e) additional storage for materials such as wood-wool, clay and tow
(f) running water, both hot and cold

Beginners in the art of taxidermy, however, may have to improvise and make do with the kitchen table covered in newspaper.

The tools required are few but they should be of good quality. Most of them can be bought from the larger branches of well-known chemists (see Appendix 4).

TOOLS

scalpel handle no. 3, blades to fit no. 10 (small)
scalpel handle no. 4, blades to fit no. 22 (large)
fine-pointed scissors, 5 in.
bull-nosed scissors, 5 in.
old kitchen scissors, 9 in.
fine-pointed forceps, 5 in.
bull-nosed forceps, 5 in.
large forceps, 12 in.
wire cutters, the electrical type
bolt croppers, 13 in.
file, flat, 9 in.
wire brush, fine wires
steel comb

chains and hooks for suspending the specimens, thus allowing the use of both hands while skinning
mounted needles
needles, various, curved and straight
dressmaking pins
paper clips
strong string
strong twine, button thread
catgut, various (fishing line)
cottons
tape measure
vice
hammers, various
hand drill and assortment of drills
electric drill and assortment of drills
chisels, various
calipers
modelling tools, obtainable from model shop (metal and wooden)
pliers, wire-cutting type
hacksaw

MATERIALS

wood-wool, or excelsior (finely shredded wood), (both fine and coarse qualities can be bought in bales)
fine hardwood sawdust, magnesium carbonate and cornmeal (absorbents used for skinning)
tow, or jute fibre
cotton-wool, or cotton batting
wire, galvanised, gauges 12, 14, 16, or as needed
wire, fine cable (when using it for small birds and mice unwind individual strands)
iron rod, $\frac{1}{4}$ in. thick or as required
nails and tacks
clay, general purpose
dental plaster
animal glue (bead glue)

beeswax
paraffin wax
rosin
paints: various oil colours as required
powder paints: burnt umber, black, white,
   blue, yellow and red
paint brushes: small, large and fine

CHEMICALS

The following chemicals can be obtained from chemists or drugstores unless otherwise stated:

Acetone A highly inflammable liquid solvent. It dissolves fats and cellulose products, and is useful for cleaning off fibre-glass resin from paintbrushes

Alcohol A clear volatile liquid also known as industrial methylated spirit. Used for preservation purposes

Alum Potassium aluminium sulphate. A common name for any series of double crystalline salts. It is used as a preservative for the skins of mammals, but it should be used with caution as it can be responsible for changing colours of skins

Arsenic Sodium arsenite is a deadly poison. It was used extensively in the nineteenth century to poison skins and was an important ingredient in the preservation of skins. It has now been replaced with powdered borax. Not only is it extremely poisonous, but it is also a painful irritant to the skin

Beeswax White or bleached beeswax is used in conjunction with paraffin wax as a modelling wax, especially for plant modelling in wax

Borax A white crystalline compound which can be used as a cleaning agent and is now used instead of arsenic to protect the skins from insect attack. If mixed with tannic acid and naphthalene, it is a good preservative for mammals and birds

Camphor A white crystalline substance with a bitter taste and aromatic smell

Canada balsam Insoluble in water. An oily or resinous ointment used to harden wax as used for the reproduction of leaves, stems and petals

Capsicum, powdered Red peppers ground into powder and used as an absorbent in preservative powder

Carbolic acid (phenol) A white crystalline solid with a carbolic smell. It is soluble in water and is corrosive and poisonous. If it is mixed with formalin, it can be used for preserving animal skins

Carbon tetrachloride A heavy colourless liquid with a sweetish smell. Very useful for removing grease and oil

Carpenter's glue/bead glue A useful additive for papier-mâché

Chloride of lime A white soluble powder used in Browne's soap-based preservative

Corrosive sublimate A very poisonous white crystalline soluble salt. Mixed with wood alcohol, it makes an excellent insect repellent when painted on exposed areas of birds, e.g. ceres, legs and feet, and noses of mammals. Specimens should be cased afterwards

Dextrin, powdered A colourless or yellowish powder resembling starch. Once mixed with water, it has many uses for the taxidermist, as it becomes a strong adhesive

Fat liquor A liquid used to replace natural oils in tanned skins, e.g. skin rugs

Fibre-glass A woven glass fabric, reinforced with resin which is used mainly in the manufacture of boats and cars. It is most useful for the casting of fish and contact casting of mammal bodies

Fleximould A compound which produces a flexible mould, and enables deep undercutting to be overcome in a one- or two-piece mould

Flock powders Fine short fibres used mainly for texturing

15

Taxidermy

Formaldehyde (formalin) A gaseous compound soluble in water with an unpleasant, irritating smell. It is useful for preserving biological specimens

Fuller's earth A variety of clay-like material which absorbs oil and grease. Used to clean oiled sea birds

Glycerine A thick, syrupy, colourless and odourless liquid. In taxidermy it can be used on bird, fish and other animal skins to prevent cracking and drying

Hydrogen peroxide A thick syrupy liquid which is used as a disinfectant and bleaching agent. When diluted with water it can whiten bones. It removes difficult blood stains from feathers successfully

Hyposulphite soda Used in preservatives

Impression compounds Duplex, used mainly in the dental trade. A cold water alginate for taking impressions of teeth, tongues and mouths

Lankrolin A lanolin based oil. When rubbed well into the flesh side of mammal skins, it replaces the natural oils and makes the skin pliable

Magnesium carbonate (heavy) A white powder used to dry the feathers of birds after washing. Can also be used for drying the fur of small mammals

Methylated spirit Wood alcohol purchased as a liquid fuel. Various uses in taxidermy

Naphthalene A white, shiny, crystalline solid with a strong smell. Excellent insect repellent

Negocoll A useful and economical moulding compound, suitable for delicate objects and soft-bodied animals

Nutgalls (oakballs) Collected from oak trees and ground into a powder. Used as an additive in preservatives

Oxymariate of mercury A highly poisonous substance used in early twentieth-century preservatives. Not used today

Papier-mâché A mixture of paper pulp, glue and whiting. A small amount of plaster will make the mixture go hard eventually. It can be used for surface coating, or it can be modelled or cast in moulds. On drying, it becomes a light tough material which can be painted or shellacked. Useful in the making of large mammal manikins. Papier-mâché can be made from this recipe:

> paper pulp
> powdered dextrin
> phenol
> plaster of Paris

Soak ordinary newspapers in water for two or three days. Then work the saturated paper with your hands or with an improvised mixing tool attached to an electric drill, until the paper turns to pulp. Add the same amount of powdered dextrin as paper pulp. (Dextrin is a carbohydrate found in the sap of plants which has an adhesive quality.) Let the mixture soak for several hours, or until the dextrin completely dissolves. If dextrin is unobtainable, use animal glue which has been melted down in a double saucepan. Add to the mixture one teaspoon of phenol. This mixture can be put in a sealed container and kept indefinitely. Remove a small portion of papier-mâché as required, and add an equal part of plaster of Paris to it. Mix this together to the required consistency. The addition of the plaster enables the mixture to dry hard.

Paraffin wax A white, translucent solid which melts to a colourless liquid; it can be used on its own, or together with other waxes, like beeswax, for making wax casts of certain objects, e.g. plants, leaves and stems

Paralene CFT Liquid used in the tanning of animal skins

Plaster of Paris A white powder used extensively for the making of various moulds. Also used to harden modelling compound and papier-mâché

Polyurethane   Caradate 30 and Bibbithane are the most useful polyurethanes

Potassium permanganate   A purple, crystalline, soluble salt. It dissolves in water to a purple solution which the taxidermist can use to stain faded antlers

P.V.C. pastes   Vycoat is an air-drying P.V.C. and Welvic paste is used as a filler

Resin   There are four resins which are most important for the taxidermist in his work on the preparation of fish and mammal manikins. They are Membrano, polyester resin, Belxona and fibre-glass

Rosin   Finely powdered, it is used as an additive to hardened wax

Rubber compounds   Silicone rubber and Revultex compound are essential for the taxidermist in the making of flexible moulds

Sal ammoniac (ammonium chloride)   A white soluble crystal used in Browne's preservative solution

Saltpetre   Potassium nitrate, a white crystalline compound used in addition to salt for pickling animal skins

Simplex rapid   An acrylic dental repair material used for making artificial tongues and gums

Sodium perborate   Perborate of soda. Mixed with boiling water it is used in the preparation of osteological specimens

Spirits of salt   Hydrochloric acid, a colourless corrosive liquid

Sublimate of sulphur   A pre-war preservative additive

Sulphuric acid   A colourless, oily liquid with a corrosive action. It is used in pickling and tanning skins. It must be treated with great care, as it burns most fabrics and can cause severe burns to the skin

Tannic acid   A yellow uncrystallised soluble solid used in tanning. Mixed with borax, it makes an excellent preservative for the skins of birds and small mammals

Tartar   Salt of tartar is a reddish-brown crystalline deposit. A preservative additive

Trichlorethylene   Obtainable in liquid form. An excellent cleaning agent for fur and feather, it can also be used for degreasing

Turpentine   A liquid extracted from the resin of pine trees. It is used as a thinning agent in oil-based paints and varnishes

Vinamould   A rubber compound which when melted can be poured over objects to make a mould. It can be re-used up to 15 times

Vinalak   Celluloid solution used to seal the insides of moulds

Wacker silicon   A silicon cold cure rubber available with several different catalysts, i.e. thick quick cure or the much slower cures

Whiting   A pure form of calcium carbonate. It is prepared by grinding chalk into a white powdery substance and mixing it with water. The taxidermist uses it as a filler in the making of papier-mâché. Also useful for the degreasing of skins

Wood-wool   A finely shredded wood which is also known as excelsior. Both fine and coarse qualities can be bought in bales and are used for the making of bird and mammal bodies. An essential commodity

Zelex   A powder which is mixed thoroughly with cold or warm water and applied to the object, brushed with a small brush into the detail. It sets rapidly to an elastic mould which must be used within thirty minutes or stored in an airtight container

Zelgan   A powder mixed with water used to make detailed moulds. Most useful for frogs and toads. Not re-usable

CARE AND MAINTENANCE

The storage and care of a collection is very

important, for if the taxidermist has done his job well, the specimens should last almost indefinitely. Obviously a collection which is well-used is less vulnerable to insect attack than one which is in permanent storage. There are, however, essential factors to recognise in the care of a collection. The specimens can be protected in a number of ways, particularly against insect attack. They must be housed in insect-proof cabinets and drawers; insect repellents should be scattered in the cabinets and within the drawers. An added safeguard is to place the specimens in polythene tubing. Constant vigilance is an important defence against insect attack. Insect damage to a single specimen can spread rapidly throughout the entire collection if it is not detected in the early stages.

Insect repellents

Naphthalene in flake form is a useful insect repellent. The flakes should be crushed to release the vapour. Vaporisation and crystallisation are likely to occur on the plumage of birds not protected by polythene bags

Paradichlorbenzene is another effective and highly volatile agent which is used extensively, though it is now regarded as responsible for bringing about colour changes in specimens (inducing foxing in browns and greys and making whites turn yellowish). Moreover prolonged exposure to its vapour is believed to involve a risk of lung cancer (see J. M. Harrison, *Bird Taxidermy*)

In no circumstances should specimens be placed in direct sunlight. If they are exposed to such extremes they will in the end fade beyond recognition. The best accommodation is a blacked-out room, illuminated only by fluorescent lights; this is not always possible, especially in museums, but an effort should be made to protect the rare specimens from the sun. Study skins kept in drawers are of course easier to protect than mounted specimens which are kept in cabinets, as there is little chance of the skins fading from sunlight.

Special care must be taken when introducing new specimens which have been received from other sources. These should be put into isolation, or fumigated immediately before inclusion in your collection. Accidental damage, especially to mounted material, should also be guarded against, as well as breakages of limbs, soiling, dampness and fading of the specimen.

4

Some Useful Tips

It is important for the beginner to be aware of certain difficulties relating to the skinning and preserving processes in taxidermy. The following instructions are therefore useful preliminaries.

ALUM

It is true that alum, potassium aluminium sulphate, has an astringent effect on the raw skins of mammals. It is also true that alum is the cause of certain colour changes in the skins of mammals. Red squirrel, *Sciurus vulgaris*, is a well-known example. So too is the fur of certain species of seal; their natural colours will change to a deep yellow.

Apart from these unsatisfactory properties, alum is an important preservative. Burnt alum (potassium aluminium ustum) is now almost impossible to obtain and potassium aluminium sulphate should be used. After using it, as instructed on p. 27, the skin will be found to be fairly stiff. The following method will make the skin clean, supple and easily manageable for mounting.

Remove the skin from the pickle and allow it to drain (flesh side out). When sufficiently dry, spread it out on your working surface and brush the hide vigorously with a wire brush, brushing out all the wrinkles. Pay particular attention to the head, neck and the parts along the incision. Every effort must be made not to stretch the skin.

Using a little soap, wash the skin until clean and then rinse thoroughly. Hang the clean skin outside and allow it partially to dry. When it is sufficiently dry, turn the skin flesh-side out and anoint it with the soap-based preservative. Sprinkle sawdust on to the preservative to contain it and to

stop spillage on to the fur. Turn the skin fur-side out and place it into a drum containing fine sawdust. Allow it to spin until dry.

Smaller mammals, such as rat, squirrel and rabbit, can be shaken in a tin or box until dry.

You will now find that the skin will have lost all the hardness caused by the alum. The soap-based preservative will help to keep it soft and supple.

SKINNING THE HEAD OF AN OWL

The head of an owl will, with a little manipulation, go down the neck skin. Great care must be taken not to stretch the skin of the neck, otherwise it will become baggy and go out of shape. Having skinned the specimen in the normal way (see Chapter 9), and with the skull inverted, we are ready to clean the skull, removing the eyes and the brain.

Do not disconnect the ears from their original position in the skull. Remove the main body bulk and also the tongue. The skull should be lying with the crown of the head down, lower mandible uppermost. Remove the hard horny palate of the upper mandible, and also that part of the cranium from the foramen magnum to where it joins the palate. The sclerotic rings of the eyes and the brain itself are now exposed. Without further ado, remove the brain.

With the brain out of the way, the bony structures at the base of the eyes should now be removed, leaving an easy exit for the eyes themselves. The main concern here is not to puncture the eyes; otherwise spillage of their contents will badly soil the feathers of the face.

Place a wad of cotton-wool in the eyes,

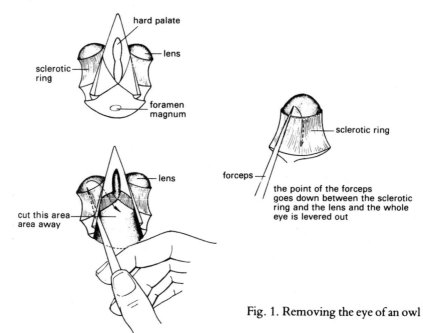

Fig. 1. Removing the eye of an owl

covering the lenses as a precaution against the possible puncturing of the eyeballs. Working from the inside of the skull, push fine-pointed forceps up alongside the sclerotic ring of the eye. On reaching its frontal edge, the forceps are levered upwards at right angles and down into the sclerotic ring itself. With the fine-pointed forceps secure, pull down and back, removing the complete eye structure.

Take out both eyes and clean any remaining flesh from the skull. Dust liberally with borax preservative.

BIRD TONGUES

A good method of reproducing the tongue of a bird artificially is to cut the required shape from the quill of a feather, fitting it into the modelled mouth. This, if done properly, produces good results, making the artificial tongue difficult to distinguish from the real tongue.

REMOVING TENDONS FROM THE LEGS OF LARGE BIRDS

It is sometimes necessary to remove the tendons from the legs of large birds such as herons, swans and geese. These tendons are removed primarily to facilitate the insertion of the supporting wires of the legs.

A cut is made in the pad of the foot. It may also be necessary to make another incision at the rear of the first joint or heel, in order to remove the large cartilaginous

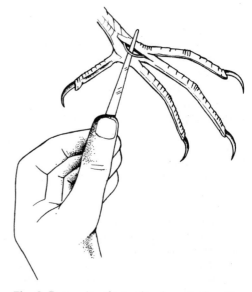

Fig. 2. Removing the tendon from the leg of a large bird

area, so making way for the wire.

A strong screwdriver is useful for the removal of the tendons. By hooking it through the sole of the foot, the tendons can be drawn down the whole length of the shank.

When the area is clean, it can be preserved with borax and tannic acid. Both incisions are sewn up for the completed specimen.

LEGS OF SHORT-WINGED HAWKS

The leg structure of such birds as sparrow-hawk or goshawk is somewhat different from that of other birds, in so much as the

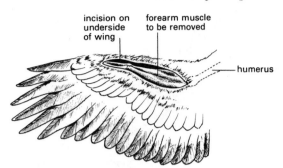

Fig. 4. Skinning the wing of a large bird

around the incision, making easy access for the removal of the forearm muscles. Using fine-pointed scissors and forceps, remove all flesh and dust liberally with borax preservative.

After preservation, the muscle can be replaced with chopped tow and the incision loosely sewn together.

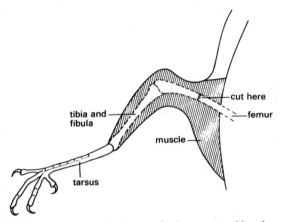

Fig. 3. Cutting the femur of a short-winged hawk

SKINNING HORNED HEADS

To skin a horned or antlered head, an incision must be made at the back of the head in order to remove the entire skull. After skinning the animal in the normal way, skin as far up the neck as possible until the antlers

femur and the tibia and fibula are exceptionally long, making the skinning of the legs rather difficult. The difficulty arises when the knee is pushed up through the incision in order to disarticulate the joints of the femur, tibia and fibula. In order to ease this situation, simply cut (with a pair of strong bull-nosed scissors) through the femur shortening it, so allowing the knee to be pushed out more easily.

SKINNING WINGS OF LARGE BIRDS

When dealing with large birds of crow size upwards, it is necessary to open the wing and make a superficial incision on the underside, from the carpal joint (wrist) to the joint of the humerus. Free the skin

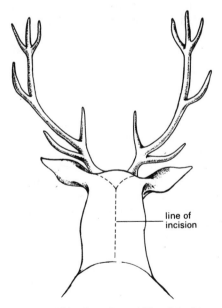

Fig. 5a. Skinning a horned head: incision

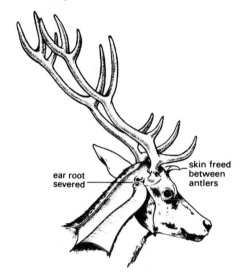

Fig. 5b. Skinning a horned head: cutting the ears

prevent any further progress. Sever the head as close to the skull as possible, and by making a y-shaped cut at the back of the neck, the whole head can be removed.

Use a sharp chisel to free the skin from around the base of the horns. The ears are cut close to the skull, and the cape or head skin can be skinned down the face towards the nose.

Deer have facial scent glands which must be skinned around with care, being winkled out from their roots deep in the muzzle. Finally, the skin is released at the mouth and nose and the skull removed.

CLEANING FUR AND FEATHER

The cleaning of fur and feather is fairly straightforward. Apply any of the following agents to the affected parts with the aid of cotton-wool. Badly soiled specimens, such as oiled birds, can be totally immersed.

Many household soap-powder products are good for the removal of superficial dirt. The affected areas should be dabbed with wet cotton-wool and wiped in the direction the fur or feathers lie.

Cold or warm water is very good for the removal of fresh blood or dirt, but is improved with the addition of a biological detergent or washing soda. After using

these products, rinse the specimen well before drying.

Hot water removes hard coagulated blood. Do not immerse the skin in the hot water. Simply dab the stained area with cotton-wool. To remove grease and oil, carbon tetrachloride, trichlorethylene or a high octane petrol B.P.4 should be used alone or can be mixed together. All three chemicals are useful in the removal of water from the feathers after washing.

Hydrogen peroxide is a useful agent, if used sparingly, for the removal of obstinate blood stains from white feathers. Dab the blood stain and when the stain is erased use clean water to wash away the peroxide. If the latter precaution is not taken, bleaching will take place, leaving an immovable stain.

Huber's cleaning mixture

petrol	5 litres
alcohol	315 ml
turpentine	65 ml

This is an excellent cleaning mixture for the removal of grease and oil on very fat wildfowl and is also useful for badly oiled specimens.

After the various cleaning agents have been used, the remaining water in the feathers must be forced out. This can be done by wiping the plumage with one of the chemicals already mentioned, such as high octane petrol B.P.4 or trichlorethylene. The specimen should then be put into a tin or box, containing heavy magnesium carbonate and the contents shaken vigorously for a few minutes. This will allow the magnesium to penetrate the feathers and dry them. Remove the skin from the box and shake off the excess magnesium. Any further dust can be blown out with compressed air or by beating with a flat stick or split cane. Final drying should be carried out with a hairdryer until the plumage is fluffy.

Larger specimens, which will not fit into a tin or box, can be dried in a cleaning drum (see Fig. 6).

The skins of mammals should go through a similar procedure. Hardwood sawdust or

dry powdered clay can be substituted for
the magnesium carbonate. Another excellent cleaning agent for fur is fuller's earth.

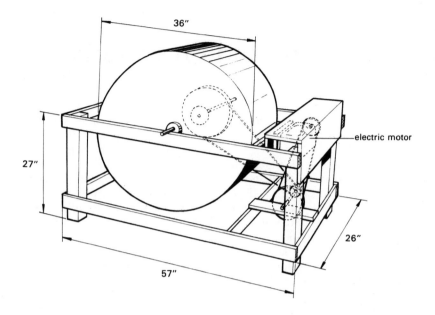

Fig. 6. Diagram of a cleaning drum

5

Fixing and Preserving

THE CAUSE OF BACTERIAL DECAY IN MAMMAL SKINS

As soon as the animal is dead, heat putrefaction begins. The hair and skin start to slip as bacteria enzymes attack the collagen round the hair follicles, and the hair becomes loose and can be pulled out. In the advanced stages of skin slipping, bacteria will attack the corium minor layer of the skin and the epidermis, causing the epidermis layer and the hairs to slip away from the corium minor at the basal membrane junction. This slipping of the epidermis will result in a hairless skin, which would be quite unsuitable for taxidermy use.

Slipping of the skin usually occurs first around the stomach area of the animal and may also occur around the eyes, ears and nose or any external haemorrhage area. In the advanced stages of decomposition the skin around the affected areas may turn green and will often produce bad odours.

Such specimens can be saved by brushing the affected areas with a strong brine solution or acetone before the skinning is done. No two skins are exactly alike, and not only slipping affects skins. Certain general factors affect the quality of all skins, such as the age of the animal when it dies, its welfare and feeding, the climatic conditions under which it lived and, of course, the season of the year, which can affect the hair or fur, causing moulting.

FIXING

As soon as the skin has been removed from the carcass, it must be washed well in cold water, to remove traces of blood and dirt from the fur. All mammal skins must be immersed in a fixing solution for a period of two to six days, depending on the thickness of the skin. This fixing solution will kill all bacteria responsible for hair and skin slipping, with the exception of halophilic

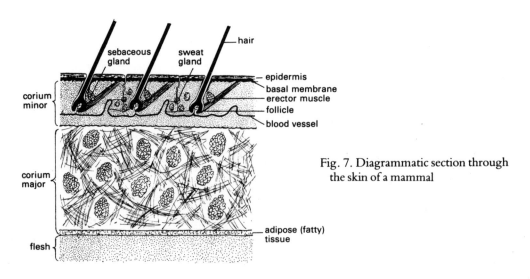

Fig. 7. Diagrammatic section through the skin of a mammal

(salt-loving) bacteria. Halophilic bacteria, however, can easily be killed by adding carbolic acid to the fixative solution. This operation of killing bacteria which decompose animal skin and tissue is known as 'fixing', indicating the fixing of the epidermis and the corium minor. When a mammal skin has been in a fixative solution the skin can be handled and worked on without fear of slipping.

There are several fixative solutions the taxidermist can use for treating mammal skins. For large mammals, the size of a rabbit or larger, I use a salt and alum fixative. This solution can be made up in large quantities at very little cost. It is very effective on the thicker and larger mammal skins that require a vast amount of the solution to cover them. The ingredients are as follows:

water	7 litres
sodium chloride (salt)	700 gm
alum	700 gm
borax	100 gm
carbolic acid	10 gm

Dissolve the salt and alum in boiling water and then add the borax and carbolic acid. Stir thoroughly until there are no chemical crystals to be seen in the solution. If the solution is tested with a brineometer it should read at around 45 per cent of the saturated solution. Once a bath of this brine solution is made up, however, a constant monthly check must be kept on its specific gravity. If the percentage has fallen, add more salt. If it has risen, add more water until the right percentage is achieved.

If the specific gravity falls below 25 per cent, bacteria may survive and will cause the epidermis to slip. If the specific gravity is higher than 60 per cent, crystallisation will occur and may cause damage to the fur or hair, for crystals are difficult to remove from the pelt. Before using a salt and alum bath, you must familiarise yourself with certain rules in order to produce good fixing results. First skin all external parts of the animal, making sure the ears, lips, feet and tail are skinned properly before immersing the skin in the solution. When placing the skin into the fixative bath,

make sure it is completely turned inside out. Spread the skin out in the bath as much as possible to eliminate any folds or doubling. Also, make sure there are no air pockets under the skin, as these may hold bacteria and may cause decomposition. The brine fixative solution must penetrate both sides of the skin, and the position of the skin in the bath must be changed. Move it up and down and around for the first day or two. This will release any air trapped underneath. Brine solutions will keep indefinitely if only washed and clean skins are put into them. Skins have been kept in this fixative solution for up to eighteen months, and when they were taken out they were as workable and fresh as a skin that had been in the bath for six days. Care must be taken never to use sea salt for the brine solutions, as this may contain halophilic bacteria which will cause slipping of the epidermis. Brine solutions must be kept in a non-corrosive container such as polythene, fibre-glass or a lead-lined tank.

Care must be taken with small mammals' skins to ensure that pelts with soft pigmentation, such as red squirrel, stoat and weasel, are not put into a brine and borax solution, as this may cause the pelt colour to fade slightly. I have had success with fixing small mammals' skins in acetone and also in methylated spirits, and have found that acetone acts very quickly on these small skins. It will penetrate the whole skin and fix successfully in a matter of two hours. Acetone will also degrease the skin, and so is better than brine and methylated spirit fixatives.

After the skins have been fixed in the solution they should feel firm and leathery to the touch. This is a good indication that the skin is fixed properly. The firm texture of the hide will make paring a straightforward operation, allowing the knife to pare the connecting tissue without sliding, as it would on an unfixed skin.

After paring, the skin should be placed into a degreasing agent such as petrol or white spirit; I prefer petrol as it takes little washing out afterwards. Skins which have gone through the fixative and degreasing solutions must be thoroughly washed in cold water to remove traces of chemicals.

PRESERVATIVES

The skin is now ready to receive the preservative, which must be used to eliminate damage to the skin and hair by moths and beetles. The most troublesome are *Tinaea pellionella, Anthrenus scrophularia, Cermestes lardiarius* and *Tineola bisselliela*.

Borax is very good as an insect deterrent and is used extensively in USA. The borax is made up in the form of a solution into which the skins are immersed.

Poisons are also good as insect deterrents but are not really suitable unless the specimen is to be sealed inside a glass case. Probably the best known preservative, even to the layman, is arsenic. Arsenic has been used for many years. It was discovered and made up by Bécoeur, who worked in the 1770s. It was Charles Waterton who said that arsenic was dangerous to the operator and inefficient as a preservative. I agree with the former part of his statement, but beg to differ with the latter. Montagu Browne, in *Practical Taxidermy*, states that he has no faith in arsenic. But he admits that arsenic dries, and that it preserves all flesh from decay better than any other known preservative, though he adds that insects are not deterred from attacking specimens so treated. Indeed, he maintains that insects eat it and become fat on it. The original formula as laid down by Bécoeur is as follows:

camphor	5 oz
powdered arsenic	2 lb
white soap	2 lb
salt of tartar	12 oz
lime or chalk	4 oz

Shred the soap and dissolve in water. When it is dissolved, add the salt of tartar and powdered chalk. Allow this mixture to cool and add the arsenic. Lastly, add the finely powdered camphor, and mix until it is the consistency of paste. Dilute the paste with a little cold water and store it in earthenware pots labelled *Poison*.

The Americans have used arsenic mixed with alum. This was said to be especially good in hot, moist climates such as South America, but the alum was inclined to make the skin very hard, especially the skins of birds, so borax was substituted and found to work better.

Chapin, an American working in the 1920s, states that arsenic should not be omitted, because of its lasting protection against insects. Make what you will from the statements of Waterton, Browne and Chapin. My own view is that arsenic is not really necessary when working for a properly organised and equipped museum. The danger of insect attack is more apparent than real. However, specimens should be placed in insect-proof cabinets and fumigated annually, which should ensure an indefinite life free from insect attack.

I have found over the years that the borax preservative is as good as any. It has the advantage of being dry and can be dusted on freely. The borax should first be rolled with a rolling pin, making it lump-free. To this fine powder, add previously rolled tannic acid and naphthalene, to the ratio of two ounces of both tannic acid and naphthalene to one pound of borax. This preservative can be used for both birds and mammals.

Preservatives for birds and small mammals

The following preservative for birds and small mammals up to rabbit size has been found over the years to be most reliable:

grated white Windsor soap	2 lb
hot water	2 pts
sodium borate (borax)	9 oz
naphthalene	3 oz
camphor	8 oz
methylated spirits	½ pt
Dettol	2 fl oz
turpentine	2 fl oz
whiting	3 lb

Dissolve the grated soap in the hot water. Add the sodium borate and the naphthalene. Dissolve the camphor in the methylated spirits and add it to the soap mixture along with the Dettol and turpentine. To thicken the mixture to the correct consistency, add the whiting. Store the preservative in stoppered jars and use when required.

Montagu Browne made up a formula

which is non-poisonous, and which I use regularly for small birds, small mammals and fish. The recipe is as follows:

whiting or chalk	2½ lb
soft soap	1 lb
chloride of lime	2 oz
camphor	1 oz
(Browne recommends tincture of musk)	

Tincture of musk is difficult to obtain and is only used to give the mixture a more pleasant smell.

Another preservative that ought to be mentioned is one that appears in Oliver Davie's *Methods in the Art of Taxidermy*. The object of this preparation is mainly to help preserve the skin of birds and small mammals and to keep them soft and supple for a few months until they can be mounted, or made into study skins at the preparator's convenience.

I used this formula in 1973 while on an expedition to the Faroe Islands. The preparation lasted for the month we were there, and the skins were easily made up on our return. After skinning, a soap-based preservative was brushed on to the inside of the skin and Davie's formula applied.

The formula is composed of two-thirds glycerine and one-third pure carbolic acid.

Phenol or carbolic acid, mixed in the same way as formalin to 2 per cent, can do the same job in the preserving of animal skins. Both formalin and phenol diluted to 2 per cent make an efficient solution to be painted on the inside of the skins of birds and small mammals.

Here is a non-poisonous preservative powder as described by Montagu Browne:

pure tannin	1 oz
red pepper	1 oz
camphor	1 oz
burnt alum	8 oz

Thoroughly mix the ingredients and keep them in stoppered bottles or canisters. This formula should only be used on the thinner skins of birds and small mammals, as it will not penetrate thick skins or sufficiently fix the fur on them. This is an insect powder and according to Montagu

Browne is an efficient substitute for snuff.

Preservatives for larger mammals

These are somewhat different from those used on the thinner skins of birds:

alum (potassium aluminium sulphate)
common salt, or
saltpetre (potassium nitrate)
phenol (carbolic acid)

Alum can be mixed with either salt or saltpetre in the ratio of one pound of alum to a quarter of a pound of saltpetre. This mixture is then rubbed into the skin. A bath of the mixture can be made up with the addition of carbolic acid. The fur of certain animals can be affected by alum. Red squirrels, in particular, will change colour to a yellowish brown if alum gets into the fur. An Atlantic grey seal, which I once worked on for Leicestershire Museums, was noticed to have a slight colour change in the spots, which was probably due to the alum.

The feet have to be relaxed if they are left for long periods before mounting. Preservatives such as full-strength formaldehyde should never be used on specimens which are to be skinned and mounted, or made up into cabinet skins. Even 2 per cent formalin is inclined to dry the thin skins of small mammals and birds. 2 per cent formalin can be used to offset decomposition in larger mammals, such as foxes and badgers.

Strong formalin can render the skeletons of specimens useless, making the bones chalky and soft. Diluted to 2 per cent, however, it makes an excellent solution for preserving the skins of larger mammals from the fox upwards. Specimens can be left in the solution for between six and twenty days, depending on the thickness of the skin. These skins should be checked daily.

The following recipe is for a general pickling solution for mammals:

water	4 gall
salt	2¼ lb
alum	¼ lb
borax	¼ lb

Taxidermy

Bring the water to the boil and add the three dry ingredients. Stir until the powders are completely dissolved. Allow the pickle to cool completely before using.

Preservatives for animal hides

water	1 gall
salt	1 qt
sulphuric acid	1 fl oz

Dissolve the salt in warm water by stirring. When completely dissolved, pour in the sulphuric acid gently, being careful not to splash this dangerous liquid.

Skins can be left in this solution for as long as a week or more without being harmed. But it is always worth remembering that salts are responsible for colour changes in certain skins, especially yellows and reds. Skins of these colours should therefore never be saturated, but simply painted on the flesh side. The thicker the skin the more often this brine has to be painted on. Thin skins will need only one application. Here is a simple tanning process:

water	1 qt
salt	1 lb
alum	1 lb
sulphuric acid	½ fl oz
flour	8 oz
hyposulphite soda	4 oz

Dissolve the water, salt and alum by boiling. Allow to cool. Then add the remaining ingredients. Stir and mix thoroughly.

Nineteenth-century preservatives

The following recipes are those that were in use throughout Britain from the early to mid-nineteenth century. As you will notice, highly poisonous chemicals were used. Here is a powder for preserving the skins of birds:

nutgalls (oak balls)	1 oz
corrosive sublimate	2 dram
white arsenic	2 dram
powdered camphor	6 dram
sal ammoniac	½ oz
powdered capsicum	½ oz

These were mixed together thoroughly and it was said to harden any small quantity of flesh which may have adhered to the skin. Below are preservatives for internal and external use.

corrosive sublimate	1 dram
spirits of salt	2 dram
spirits of camphor	6 oz

The corrosive sublimate was dissolved in the spirits of camphor and the spirits of salt were then added, to be brushed on to the skins before mounting. This was said to be useful for both birds and mammals.

corrosive sublimate	1 dram
wood alcohol	as required

Place corrosive sublimate into a vessel and add a small amount of wood alcohol. To test the mixture dip in the tip of a black feather. If, after taking the feather out and allowing it to dry, a white deposit can be seen, then more alcohol must be added until the feather dries its natural colour.

The next recipe is very old and some of the materials will be very hard to obtain. But it is interesting to note what recipes were used for preserving fish and reptiles before the advent of modern techniques.

burnt alum in powder	3 oz
sublimate of sulphur	2 oz
oxymariate of mercury	½ oz
camphor in powder	½ oz
oak or elm bark in powder	4 oz

Mix these ingredients together and dress the fish or reptile with it before mounting.

Finally, a classic recipe for a soap-based preservative which, it is said, will preserve almost anything, concocted by an apothecary at Mentz in Germany:

chalk in powder	6 oz
camphor	5 oz
arsenic	2 lb
white soap	2 lb
salt of tartar	12 oz
sugar in powder	12 oz

This is made in the same way as our present-day soap-based preservatives. The instructions for use are as above.

If you do make use of it, take care to wear a pair of soft leather gloves, or it will get under the fingernails. I need hardly point out the consequences of neglecting this precaution.

ANTLERS

Preserving antlers in velvet

Mix three parts of 6 per cent formaldehyde solution with 97 parts of water. The velvet-covered antlers should then be submerged in this solution and left for seven to ten days, checking daily. Alternatively, drill a hole through the centre core of the growing antler and inject the solution. This must be done daily, allowing the solution to penetrate the soft antler.

Colour restoration of bleached antlers

Dissolve one teaspoon of potassium permanganate in half a cup of warm water. Mix and apply to a small area of the antler. If the solution is too dark, add more water. If the area is too light, add a few more drops of potassium permanganate.

The preservatives that have been mentioned are virtually all the preparator requires. Larger mammals, such as big cat and deer, after being measured and skinned, can be packed off to the tanner to be dressed for mounting or tanned for rug making (the tanner must be informed of your intentions).

6

Moulding and Casting

Moulding and casting are techniques used in the production of one or more copies of an object. A mould is a negative shape; a cast is a positive shape.

TYPES OF MOULDS

Rigid moulds

Draw-mould: a one-piece mould where only one face of the original is required and where no undercutting is present, e.g. one side of a flat-fish.

Piece-mould: a mould composed of two or more interlocking pieces to overcome undercutting, e.g. fungi.

Waste-mould: a mould which is destroyed to separate the cast. The original object must be flexible or capable of being melted or dissolved out, e.g. frog or toad.

Squeeze-mould: a one or two-piece mould where pressure is applied to shape the cast, e.g. wax leaf or petal.

Flexible moulds

Flexible moulds enable deep undercutting to be overcome in a one- or two-piece mould. Each type of material has special properties and applications. Examples are polyvinyl chlorides (Vinamould, Fleximould, Castogel), glue-gelatine, Negocoll, Zelex, rubber latex (lasting flex).

Special applications

Enlarged or reduced moulds may be produced by immersing polyvinyl chlorides or lasting flex in suitable solvents. Lasting flex (American latex) expands in paraffin. Vinamould and Fleximould expand in amyl acetate. Vinamould and Fleximould contract in toluol.

NOTES ON MOULDING AND CASTING MATERIALS

Plaster (moulding and casting)

White or dental plaster should be used. Mix with cold water to a consistency of cream and apply to object, brushing in with a small brush to ensure complete cover. Set up retaining walls if required. This plaster sets in ten to fifteen minutes. To prevent air bubbles use 5 per cent wetting agent – Wettol, Johnson's 326 and other wetting agents – instead of water. This slows down the setting time to about one hour and permits a thicker mixture. Note that the thicker the mixture, the harder the resultant plaster. To harden, treat with vinyl acetate dissolved in toluol or boil in diluted borax solution; it is important to note that cracking of thin parts may occur with this solution. When casting plaster to plaster, use oil or preferably liquid soap as a releasing agent. For coarse details only, shellac dissolved in methylated spirits is satisfactory.

Before painting plaster casts with watercolours, treat with size solution. When using oil paints treat with size or vinyl acetate in toluol.

Vinamould (moulding)

Melt in an oil bath or over an asbestos mat to prevent burning. Warm the object to be cast and pour Vinamould over it, using retaining walls where necessary. Vinamould sets on cooling to a firm elastic mould, and cooling may be accelerated by immersion in cold water. The object must be thoroughly dry and nonporous due to the high melting point of Vinamould (150 °C). If the object is porous, such as plaster and wood, seal thoroughly with celluloid solution or Vinalak 5906. Vinamould is sold in three grades – soft, medium and hard – which may be re-used up to fifteen times before becoming too thick for use. Vinamould may then be softened by stirring a small amount of liquid paraffin into the melted compound. The grades may be mixed and the soft grade is obviously the most economical. For enlarging and reducing moulds ask for Patent Specification No. 25937/48. Fleximould is a very similar moulding compound.

Rubber latex (moulding)

A natural milky latex preserved in suspension by ammonia or amides, and setting to solid rubber on drying. If pure latex is used, the final product is transparent, but it is better to add filler which results in an opaque rubber when dry. Apply with a brush to the object, giving several thin coats and allowing each coat to dry.

This mould is extremely elastic and may be everted through a small hole to remove the object. It gives excellent reproduction of fine detail, and like Vinamould, may be used for making hundreds of casts before loosing quality.

It is particularly useful for rigid undercut objects, especially ivory and metals, but the ammonia discolours copper. It will not adhere to most materials, so no insulation is necessary when casting in other materials from a latex mould. There are many brands of rubber latex obtainable from various sources, but the most useful is undoubtedly the American product, 'Lasting flex' or 'Anode 10099' which is not currently available on the British market.

Zelgan (moulding)

Mix the powder thoroughly with cold or warm water to a consistency of cream and apply to the object, brushing with a small brush into the detail. Speed and accuracy in amounts is needed. It gives very sharp impressions and does not adhere to any material; it is useful for delicate objects and soft-bodied animals, and it will permit deep undercutting to be cast. The mould may be fractured to release the object and fitted together without a visible junction. Zelgan cannot be re-used and therefore is expensive in large quantities.

Beeswax and paraffin wax (moulding and casting)

Melt to a liquid which may be brushed or poured over the object with retaining walls where necessary. Use at temperatures above 60 or 70 °C and preferably warm the objects before application to prevent lines of solidification. The wax sets on cooling. Paraffin wax is slightly more transparent and less flexible than beeswax. The melted wax may be coloured by stirring in oil paint; it contracts slightly on cooling. It is, however, not very useful moulding material, and rather delicate as a casting compound. When strengthened with bolting silk it is very suitable for modelling botanical material or for making squeeze-impressions of leaves. It is obtainable in various grades and qualities from general sources.

Zelex (moulding)

Mix the powder thoroughly with cold or warm water to a consistency of cream and apply to the object, brushing with a small brush into the detail. Zelex sets in four minutes to an elastic mould which must either be used within half an hour or stored in an airtight container as it shrinks on drying.

It gives very sharp impressions and will not adhere to any material. It is useful for delicate objects and soft-bodied animals, and will permit deep undercutting. The mould may be fractured to release the object and fitted together without visible junction. It cannot be re-used and therefore is expensive in large quantities.

Negocoll (moulding)

Melt in a water bath (double saucepan) to

prevent burning. At 90 °C it gives a creamy liquid which may be brushed on to the object. As the Negocoll cools in the pan it thickens slightly but may be applied down to 45 °C. It gives very sharp impressions on cooling and will not adhere to any material. Cooling may be accelerated by immersion in water. The mould is elastic and firm and should be kept in an airtight container to prevent shrinkage.

Negocoll may be re-used indefinitely, thinning with water when it becomes too thick. A most useful and economical moulding compound, suitable for delicate objects and soft-bodied animals. For deep undercutting the mould may be fractured and fitted together invisibly with pins. Negocoll does not adhere to set Negocoll.

Gelatine (moulding)

Printer's roller gelatine is probably the most useful form of the material for moulding. It is melted in a double pan to prevent burning. It is used at temperatures above 60 °C and the object should preferably be warmed before application. Brush well in and set up retaining walls where necessary. Gelatine sets on cooling to give a firm elastic mould which keeps well and may be used for making many casts. Printer's roller gelatine may be re-melted indefinitely, thinning with a little water as required. It is similar in consistency and application to Vinamould.

Celluloid (casting)

Pyroxylin dissolved in butyl acetate is probably the most satisfactory celluloid for casting purposes. Brush the viscous solution well into a wet plaster mould and allow to dry. Give repeated coats until a sufficient thickness is obtained, allowing it to dry between each coat. As there is contraction on drying it is not suitable for casting from moulds with undercutting. If desired the cast may be painted from behind or the successive layers of celluloid may be appropriately coloured with pigments or dyes to give depth to the colouring. This method has been very successfully applied to casting amphibians, reptiles and fishes in America, and a similar method has been tried in the Royal Scottish Museum, Edinburgh. Celluloid is obtainable from chemists.

Perspex (casting)

Perspex may be dissolved in chloroform and used like celluloid in casting with slightly less contraction. It softens with heat and impressions may be made in it by pressing against a suitable heated object in a heated vice. Very satisfactory leaf casts may be made by pressing sheet perspex between heated metal dies.

7

Anatomy

Taxidermists must familiarise themselves with the basic elements of bird and mammal anatomy before commencing work. The formation of a natural balance in any mounted specimen depends on a detailed understanding of limb placement, head position, muscle shape and general attitude – in short on a knowledge of how the skeleton and both the visceral and muscular elements of the body fit together to build the living form. The skeleton is the formation on which the muscular architecture is structured. It governs the overall shape of the subject, and its importance cannot be overemphasised. Although skeletons of both birds and mammals are built on the same general plan, there are important differences between them.

MAMMALS

For purposes of description the skeleton is usually divided into two parts, the *axial* and the *appendicular*.

The axial skeleton consists of the skull, backbone, tail, ribs and breastbone. The front part of the skull is so shaped as to form the background of the face. The whole of the skull rotates on the atlas, which is the first vertebra on the spinal column. The units of the vertebrae that make up the spinal column vary in number but are grouped as follows: cervical (neck), thoracic (chest), sacral or pelvic (loins), and caudal (tail).

Running through the centre of all the vertebrae, except those of the tail, is the spinal cord, terminating in the brain. The

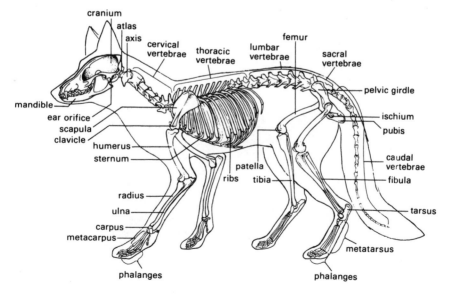

Fig. 8. Skeleton of a typical mammal

ribs form the boundaries of the chest wall; they protect the internal organs and also articulate with the vertebral column in the dorsal region. The middle ribs are joined at their lower ends to the breastbone, or sternum. In mammalian quadrupeds the pelvic girdle is made up of three fused bones, the ilium, ischium and pubis. The ilium is firmly connected to the sacrum, a variable number of fused vertebrae in the spinal column, so forming an extensive and rigid structure that lends great strength to the hindquarters and so provides a sound base on which the leg can articulate.

The appendicular skeleton comprises the limbs. The powerful hind legs are made up of a series of bones. The femur carries the strong thigh muscles, while the tibia and fibula carry a much thinner muscle. At the junction of the thigh and shin there is the patella or knee-cap. The foot is composed of a series of small bones, known as the metatarsal bones, and characteristically the digits or toes, each made up of a varying number of smaller bones, known as phalanges. There is, of course, great variation in the toe structure of both birds and mammals, and this is an important key to their classification. The front limbs of a mammal are in general not as sturdily built as the hind limbs. The humerus, or upper arm, articulates at one end with the scapula or shoulder blade and at the other with the radius and ulna, which form the forearm. The carpal joint, or wrist, is the beginning of bones known as the metacarpal bones, including the digits or toes of the forefoot. The tail is also important. Its function varies from species to species. It is used for balance, as a rudder to aid swimming, or simply as a means of warning its own kind of danger.

BIRDS

The axial skeleton of a bird is exactly the same as for a mammal. The skull is largely built up of a series of small plates which are fused together and is designed to grasp and tear, rather than to crush and chew. The mandible is divided into several portions, the front part, called the dentary, is the basis of the lower beak or bill. The upper beak is based on a bone called the maxilla. There is no false palate in birds, so the internal nostril opens into the mouth.

A bird's skull has to combine size with lightness. The bones are almost of a paper-thinness and will fracture quite easily when the bird flies into some hard object.

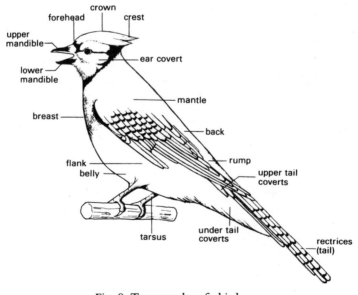

Fig. 9. Topography of a bird

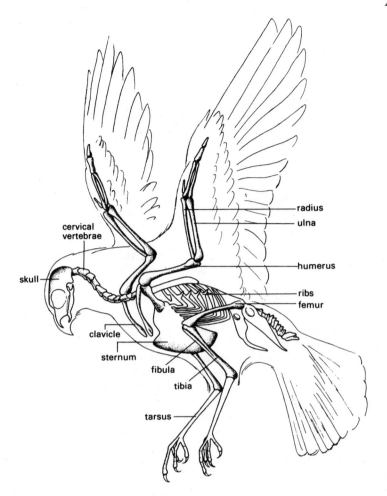

Fig. 10. Skeleton of a typical bird

The units of vertebrae that make up the spinal column vary in number but are grouped in the same way as for mammals. The number of neck vertebrae varies from thirteen to twenty-three in different species, whereas mammals almost invariably have seven.

The leg of the flying bird is a highly developed structure. The free position of the leg is divided into three main parts, known usually as the thigh, the leg or shank and the foot.

The thigh contains the femur, which at its upper end forms a good ball-and-socket joint with the hip bone. At the junction of the thigh and the leg or shank there is the knee-cap, or patella, as in mammals. The shank is composed of two fused bones: the tibia and fibula. The foot is composed of a long bone known as the tarso-metatarsus (tarsus), terminating in a series of small bones forming the toes or digits; these again are broken down into smaller bones known as phalanges.

8

Recording Data

Before proceeding to work on your specimen, it is important to record all the relevant data, which include measurements and weight. Great care must be taken when handling bird specimens, as it is extremely easy to damage the plumage. Measurements should be taken in millimetres and weight in grams. Make a point of using the same method of measuring on every occasion.

The measuring equipment should be of good quality and must be looked after carefully. The rule, either metal or transparent plastic, should have a small stop at the zero end. It is important to have a pair of dividers and a pair of slide calipers which are free running. A measuring tape is essential for measuring the larger mammals. A notebook and pencil will complete the equipment necessary for recording measurements.

THE LABEL

As far as museums are concerned, the collection of the relevant data from the dead specimen is probably the most important part of the whole process. In *Methods of Collecting and Preserving Vertebrate Animals*, R. M. Anderson states that a good label without a specimen has a certain value, but a specimen without a label has almost none.

Since labels are so important, they should be of a neat, manageable size, about 70–75 mm by 15–20 mm, with a reinforced hole for the string. Data should be written in block capitals in waterproof or Indian ink, for if ordinary ink is used and the label becomes damp, the ink will smudge, rendering the label illegible. The label should be of a high quality parchment paper or one of the strong plastics now used by museums. When writing the label, keep the string on the left, as this makes reading it easier. Obviously, all the information below will not go on to the label accompanying the specimen. Hence the need for a data book or day book, which holds the records of each individual specimen complete with its number.

The following are the important points to record:

(a) the common name of the species, followed by the scientific name

(b) the sex, and development of the gonads, after confirmation by dissection. It is useful also to include a drawing of the sex organs

(c) the age, whether adult or juvenile, and the condition of the skull, i.e. SFO (skull fully ossified) or SNFO (skull not fully ossified)

(d) the place where the specimen was found. Include a map reference with the altitude, and also a hint of the habitat – whether coastal, woodland or savanna

(e) the date, month and year the speci-

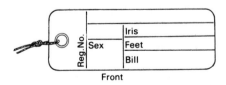
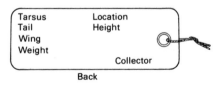

Fig. 11. Format for a label (for a bird)

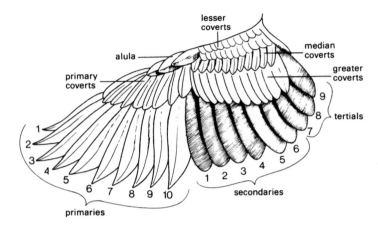

Fig. 12. Nomenclature of the wing feathers

men was obtained

(f) the measurements: for birds, the wing, tail, bill, tarsus, total length and weight; for mammals, the head, body, tail, ear, hind foot, total length and weight

(g) the colours of any area which is not covered by either fur or feather and which may loose its natural colour, e.g. for mammals: eyes and lips; and for birds: iris, bill, feet and wattles

(h) the contents of the stomach, to determine what food the bird or mammal had been feeding on

(i) the collector's name

If the specimen is of such poor quality that it cannot be used as a cabinet skin or a full mount, all is not lost, for the bones can be saved to form additional collections, ideal for reference and for teaching purposes. Skull, sternum, wings and feet are all valuable items to collect from the decomposing specimen, not to mention the complete skeletal frame, if there are no badly broken bones. All specimens should be deloused and a collection of the ecto-parasites made, together with full data. Remember that if a dead specimen is left in a freezer for a long period, it will most certainly shrink. So, from this aspect alone, measurements should be taken as soon after death as possible. Shrinkage will only be slight, but this does make a difference.

MEASURING BIRDS

There are many different methods of measuring birds and mammals. For birds, probably the best-known and most scientific reference is Witherby's *Handbook of British Birds*. Consult also *The Bird in the Hand* by Cornwallis and Smith, *Measurements of Birds* by Baldwin and *Identification for Ringers*, vols 1-3, by K. Williamson, all of which describe standard measuring methods.

The wing of a bird can be measured in various ways, but as it is probably one of the most important measurements of a bird a standard method is essential. A more recent book incorporating all the above references is *The Identification Guide to European Passerines* by L. Svensson. The methods described there are adopted by all ringers and by the British Trust for Ornithology. Natural history preparators would be well advised to adopt these methods and to standardise measurements nationally.

Wing

The wing measurement is taken when the wing is at rest. Measure from the carpal joint to the end of the longest primary feather. Take the specimen in the left hand, head towards the wrist. Bring the rule up under the wing and slide it up until the stop comes against the outer edge of the carpal

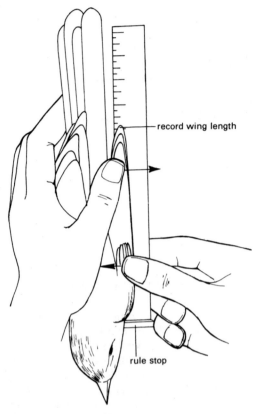

Fig. 13. Measuring the wing

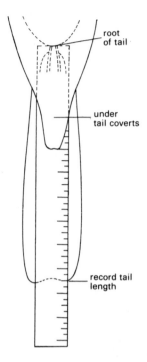

Fig. 14a. Measuring the tail

joint. The thumb of the left hand should guide the primaries, pressing down and away from the bird's body. The thumb of the right hand should apply pressure to the area of the primary coverts and push inwards towards the bird's body. While gripping the wing and the rule firmly with the right hand, stroke the thumb of the left hand along the primaries to ensure maximum length before reading the measurement.

Tail

The measurement required here is the total length of the tail from the root to the tip of the longest tail feathers. Many preparators bend the tail at right angles to the body and, using dividers, measure from the right angle to the longest tail feathers. L. Svensson describes his method as follows: passing the thin transparent ruler between the under-tail feathers and the tail itself and pushing the ruler gently up to the root of the middle tail feathers, record the measurement. This is done by simply measuring along the long axis of the tail, i.e. to the tip of the longest tail feather. With rounded or forked tails an extra measurement is required (Fig. 14b).

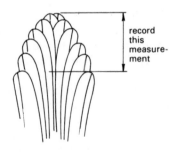

Fig. 14b. Measuring the tail: an extra measurement for forked or rounded tails

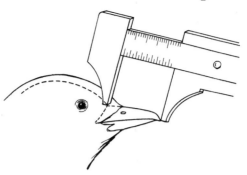

Fig. 16a. Measuring the bill: length

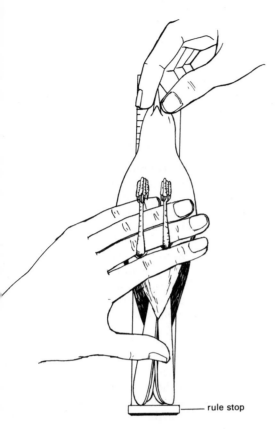

— rule stop

Fig. 15. Measuring the total length

tip of the bill is not abnormal or broken. Measurements should be taken along the top of the upper mandible or 'culmen', either from the start of the feathers to the tip, or from the skull to the tip. Place the first point of the calipers against the skull or feather line. Then gently push the second or moving point to the tip of the bill, so recording the measurement. It may be necessary to measure the depth of the bill (Fig. 16b).

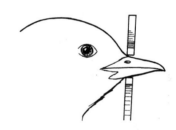

Fig. 16b. Measuring the bill: depth

Tarsus

Using your slide calipers again, measure from the notch at the back of the intertarsal joint, to the last scale at the bottom of the tarsus before the toes. The toes should be

Total length

Lay the ruler on the working surface. The specimen can be placed upon it with its back down. The tip of the tail must come up against the stop. Hold the bird by the legs, and the thumb can be used to secure the tail (holding it firmly to the ruler). The other hand is used to hold the bill (by pressing it backwards and downwards until it comes parallel with the ruler). Now record the measurement. The specimen must not be stretched, but must lie on the ruler in its own natural relaxed position. This measurement is not normally required by the taxidermist. On the other hand the more complete the data the better.

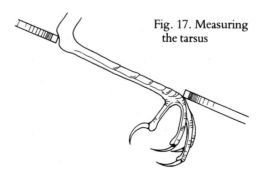

Fig. 17. Measuring the tarsus

Bill

The best instrument for measuring the bill is an easy-running set of calipers, with their outer edges pointed. Check that the

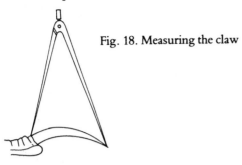

Fig. 18. Measuring the claw

bent at right angles to the tarsus, thus exposing the scale edge. To measure the claw, record the length of the exposed claw.

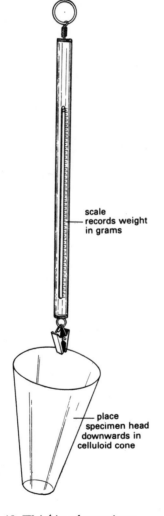

scale records weight in grams

place specimen head downwards in celluloid cone

Fig. 19. Weighing the specimen

Weight

The specimen should be weighed as soon after death as possible. Specimens left in the freezer for long periods will not give a true weight.

Sexing

It is vital to the collection of data for all specimens to be sexed internally, even if the specimen is showing plumage signs of sex.

After removing the skin, place the carcase on its back, and with a pair of scissors cut along the right hand side from the vent through the ribs to the coracloid. Push the intestines to one side and locate the kidneys, which lie close to the backbone. It is on the anterior border of the kidneys that the sex organs will be located.

In the breeding season these organs are well developed and easily identifiable. But outside the breeding season immature birds and specimens with internal injuries will cause some difficulty. If neither organ can be seen, look either for the oviduct of the female or for the two sperm ducts of the male.

The ovaries of the female are usually developed on the left side of the body only, and are recognised without too much difficulty as a series of minute egg yolks forming a granulating mass. They are cream in colour. Leading from the ovaries is a single tube, or oviduct, which goes into the cloaca.

The male organs, or testes, lie on either side of the mid-line. These are oval in shape and vary in colour from pale cream to bluish-grey. Persons not familiar with the sexing of specimens can confuse the testes with adrenals, which are almost the same colour but lie much higher in the body cavity.

Ageing

A useful exercise when dealing with passerine birds is to make a note of their age. This can be done in a number of ways. A well-known dimorphism is plumage differences. Another is skull ossification. The pneumatisation of the skull roof is a

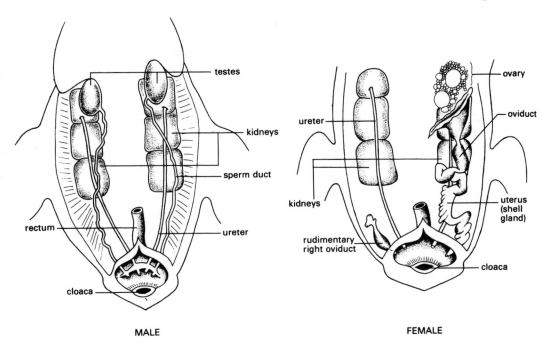

Fig. 20. Sexing

useful guide for the ageing of passerines. Skull ossification provides a point of reference when checking the other ageing criteria. It takes about four to eight months for the skull to become fully ossified. But there are some exceptions. L. Svensson wrote a paper in 1953 saying that it can be as little as two months with *Hippolais icterina*. Much work remains to be done in this field to establish a full range of species.

The exposed skull of a juvenile bird appears uniformly pinkish or reddish. The skull of the adult bird, however, is whitish or pinkish white, which is finely speckled with white dots. These dots are formed by the ends of the bony columns between the two layers of the skull. Much experience is needed when assessing the exact age by this method, but coupled with the other criteria it is most useful. There are a few records of second calendar year birds having small parts of the skull still unossified. These birds are probably from late broods. This phenomenon of early or late hatching is a point to be remembered. The diagrams below give a guide to ossification from juvenile to adult.

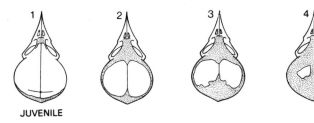

Fig. 21. Progressive ossification of the skull

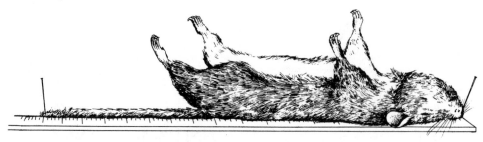

Fig. 22. Measuring the total length

MEASURING MAMMALS

Total length

The easiest and most accurate way to measure total length of a mammal is to lay the specimen on its back and force the head backwards. Place a pin at the tip of the nose and another at the tip of the tail (at the tip of the last vertebra, not the tip of the terminal hairs). The distance between these two points can now be measured and recorded. This is not practical with the larger mammals, however, the use of a measuring tape being best for these.

Head and body

Keep the specimen on its back and place a pin at the tip of the nose and the base of the tail. Measure and record.

Tail

I find it easiest to suspend the body of the specimen over the edge of a table and place a pin at the tip of the last vertebra.

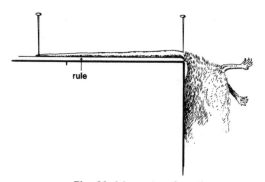

rule

Fig. 23. Measuring the tail

Hind foot

With the foot flat on the table, place a pin at the heel and another at the end of the longest toe (not the claw).

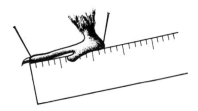

Fig. 24. Measuring the hind foot

Ear

With the ear in its natural position, using dividers, measure from the bottom of the notch to the top of the ears.

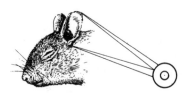

Fig. 25. Measuring the ear

Weight

Weigh the specimen and record the weight in grams.

9

Skinning Birds

The fresh specimen should be handled with great care, since rough handling may result in the plumage becoming soiled from blood or mucus leaking from the mouth or vent. Feathers may be rubbed against obstacles, so that the barbules are damaged or even the quills broken. While inspecting the specimen, check for broken wings and legs. Wipe out the mouth with cotton-wool, leaving a clean wad inside. Also, place a wad in the vent. If blood is seeping from this area, dab it with cotton-wool and sprinkle some fine hardwood sawdust on the wound. Should the eye-balls be punctured, remove the remaining liquid and plug the eye with cotton-wool. Remember to record all the scientific data of the specimen before you begin to skin the bird.

Most antiquarian books on taxidermy suggest that you should clean the plumage before skinning. Personally I prefer to do the cleaning afterwards – simply because, if the specimen becomes soiled during skinning, it will most certainly have to be washed again. Amateurs will find some difficulty in keeping the specimen perfectly clean. If there are large areas of blood, dirt or oil, however, most of it can be removed before skinning. To help you remove the skin successfully, part the feathers from breast to vent, and if you find that the skin is somewhat decomposed and the epidermis is coming away, dab the area with 40 per cent alcohol or methylated spirits. This will make the skin rather stiff and you will be able to make your incision without too much difficulty.

Though the ability to make up a good skin comes only with practice, attention to the following points will help to prevent any extra work.

1. Take care to avoid soiling the feathers with blood or mucus. The throat should be plugged with cotton-wool to prevent soiling from the stomach contents. Eyes and nostrils should be lightly dusted with fine sawdust or powdered magnesium carbonate, and shot holes either dusted or plugged.

2. Make the initial incision as small as possible and use fine sawdust or other absorbents freely so as to absorb the body fluids.

3. All fat must be removed from the skin and if this is not done thoroughly the skin will deteriorate, whichever preservative is used. Removing fat from the skins of large mammals, and birds such as ducks is a special problem. Pay particular attention to the feather tracts of birds, freeing the connective tissue from the feather stubs with a small wire brush.

4. When working with birds take care not to cut the quills at the base of the tail.

5. Pull the ear sac from the skull, but do not cut it out.

6. Take care not to cut off the eyelids.

7. In skinning birds, leave in the skull and skin to the base of the bill, taking care not to detach the skin from the gape. Remove the contents of the skull and any flesh adhering to it.

By following the sequence below and remembering the points raised above, the mechanical part of taxidermy, i.e. the skinning, should be made easier.

VENTRAL INCISION

Make sure you have all the necessary equipment to hand, Get yourself into a

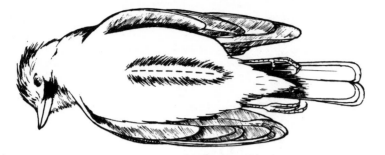

Fig. 26. First ventral incision

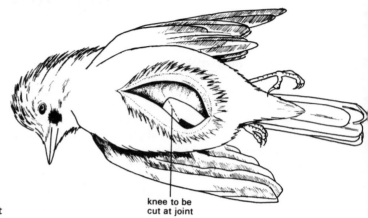

knee to be
cut at joint

Fig. 27. Exposing the knee-joint

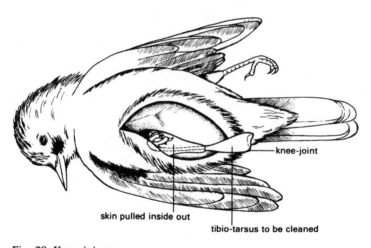

knee-joint

skin pulled inside out

tibio-tarsus to be cleaned

Fig. 28. Knee-joint cut

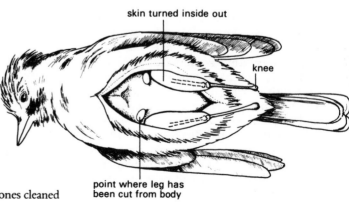

skin turned inside out

knee

point where leg has
been cut from body

Fig. 29. Both knee-joints cut and bones cleaned

comfortable position with enough light on the subject. Newspaper or clean white paper should be placed on the working surface and the specimen laid on it. If you are right-handed, place the specimen on its back with the head to the left, tail to the right. Part the feathers of the breast from mid-sternum to vent.

Taking the scalpel, gently cut through the skin. Avoid cutting too deeply, otherwise you will expose the gut and cause yourself a lot of trouble. Now, with your left hand take hold of the skin and, with your forceps or another blunt instrument, free it along the incision line. Work as far down the sides as you can, not forgetting to free the skin up the breast bone towards the throat, After freeing it all round the body, you should be able to see the knee-joint (see Fig. 27). Take hold of the tarsus and gently push the knee upwards through the incision. As you go, free the skin from around the leg. When it is sufficiently exposed, cut through the knee-joint (see Fig. 28), pulling the tibia and fibula out. All flesh can now be cleaned off these bones (see Fig. 29).

Repeat this operation on the other leg. Before concentrating on the tail, continue to free the skin down beyond the knee-joint towards the pelvic girdle. This will help when you come to the tail, which is probably the most difficult part of the skinning operation. If you have freed the skin as instructed, the tail operation should be fairly straightforward.

Pick up your specimen and place it on its breast with the head and neck resting on the table.

With the first and second fingers of the left hand placed over the vent, but inside the skin, and the thumb at the back of the tail, pressure can be exerted on the 'cloaca', (the last part of the gut), making it easy to cut through with your scalpel. The tail will not yet be freed. Taking your round-ended scissors, push the blades either side of the backbone until they can be felt with the thumb. Gently cut through the backbone. The tail skin is now almost free. A firm grip can be taken at the root of the tail and the body eased free. At this stage, you can continue to skin with one hand, while the other holds the body, or hooks and chains

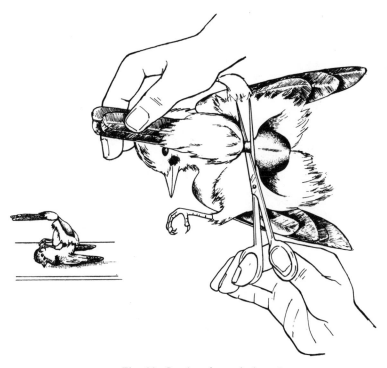

Fig. 30. Cutting through the tail

45

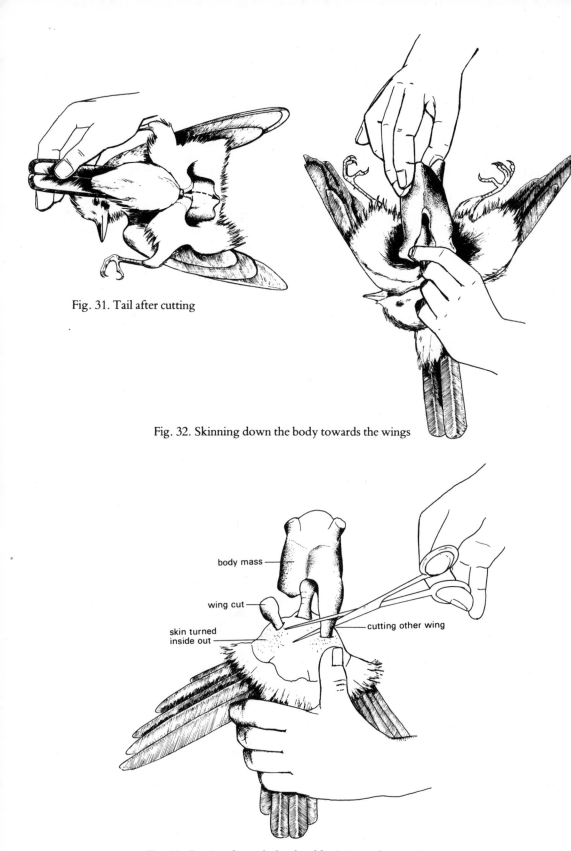

Fig. 31. Tail after cutting

Fig. 32. Skinning down the body towards the wings

body mass

wing cut

skin turned
inside out

cutting other wing

Fig. 33. Cutting through the shoulder joints, releasing the wings

46

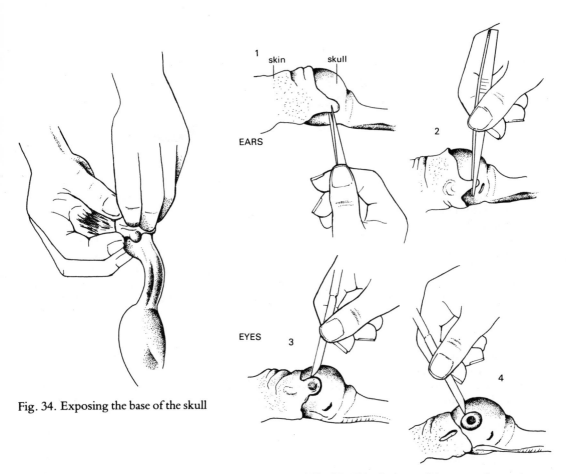

Fig. 34. Exposing the base of the skull

Fig. 35. Skinning round the ears and eyes

can be employed to suspend the bird, which will allow both hands to remove the skin. After you have freed the skin from the back of the body, the next obstacles are the wings. As long as you skin round the shoulders, however, there should be no difficulty. Simply expose these joints and cut them through. Tuck the wing bones back into the skin ready to be cleaned at a later stage.

Once both wing bones are detached, continue skinning up the neck towards the head. The head is the most important part of the specimen and, as the feathers in this region are rather short, great care must be taken not to cut the skin, mistakes being very difficult to camouflage. Manipulation with the fingers will bring out the base of the skull. As you continue, you will find the skin held firmly to the skull by the ears. These can often be pulled out by pushing the forceps into the orifice and pulling out

the ear tube. After freeing both ears, the next and last obstacles are the eyes. Cutting through the eye membrane successfully comes only with experience. But if you take your time and watch exactly what you are doing, you will be successful. A small plug of cotton-wool, placed into the eye before skinning, is useful as it can be seen through the transparent membrane. Once the skin has been freed from round the eye, slight tension on the skin will expose the transparent area where a small cut is made. The orbital ring and eyelashes can now be seen. Extend the incision to expose the complete eyeball.

Repeat this procedure on the other eye. Release the skin as far as the base of the bill. The main body bulk can now be detached, and placed on one side for future use.

The task of cleaning the inside of the skin can now begin. As the skull is already inverted, this is as good an area to begin

47

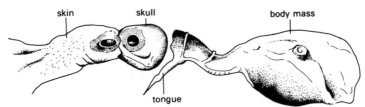

Fig. 36. Removing the body mass and tongue

working on as any. First, remove the eyeballs by placing the forceps at the back of them. You will find that they will lever out quite easily. Secondly, if the tongue has not been removed already with the body bulk, make two cuts with the scalpel along the underside of the lower mandible and remove the tongue. The cheeks and the brain must be dealt with next. A pair of strong scissors is needed to cut through both sides of the lower mandible and across the lower part of the skull. With this area removed, the brain can easily be extracted. Removing this part of the lower mandible allows easy access later when filling the cheeks.

The wings of the bird should be skinned in much the same way as the legs. When the joint with the radius and ulna is reached, the large upper-arm muscle can be cut off.

The next task is to remove the flesh from between the radius and ulna (forearm). This can be done in one of two ways. First, by loosening the skin from around these bones the flesh is exposed and can be re-moved by means of fine scissors and a pair of forceps. On no account must the secondary feathers be detached from the ulna, or difficulties will arise when mounting. If the secondaries are dislodged they will hang limp and create all sorts of frustration. Secondly, for larger specimens, the flesh can be removed from between the radius and ulna by making an incision on the underside of the wing.

Having thoroughly cleaned both wings, proceed with the tail. Push the skin off the tail feathers until the preen gland is reached. This is situated on the upper surface of the tail feathers and appears as a small creamy reservoir which must be cut away with the scalpel. The flesh around and between the tail feathers can now be removed by gently scraping with the scalpel. Finally, brush along the quill ends with a wire brush.

Removing body fat

In passerine birds the skin fats will adhere mainly to the feather tracts. These are the areas in which the feathers are concentrated.

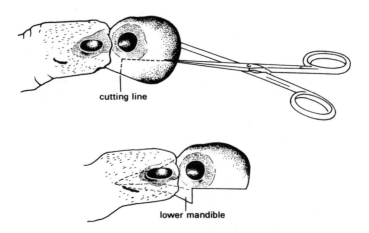

Fig. 37. Cutting through the lower mandible and skull to remove the brain

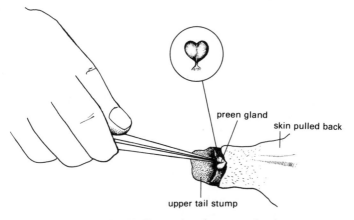

Fig. 38. Removing the preen gland

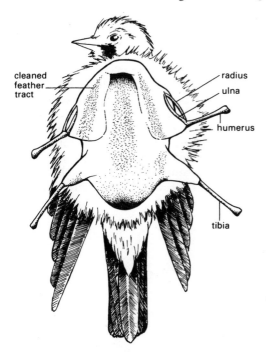

Fig. 39. Cleaning the feather tracts

fine sawdust helps to dry up any liquid grease. If, after finishing the degreasing process, some of the feathers have become soiled, the entire skin should be immersed in a container of trichlorethylene, or good clean petrol, e.g. B.P.4. Leave submerged for a few minutes and dry as normal.

Cleaning the fat from bird skins is a tiresome process which takes a great deal of time. To add to the frustration, the skin is usually tender and easily holed. Before attempting to clean the feathers, the skin must be inverted, with feathers the right-

The fat can first be removed by scraping with the back of a blunt knife and later with the wire brush. Fat which lies along the edges of the incision, around the leg skin and between the feather tracts, can usually be pulled and scraped off with the fingers.

Waterfowl, however, show no feather tracts and are therefore much more difficult to clean. The upper layer of fat can be pulled off by hand, but the remainder must be systematically removed with scissors and a wire brush. Constant dusting with

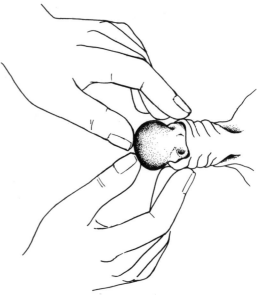

Fig. 40. Pushing the cleaned skull back into the head skin

49

side out. The cleaned skull is pushed up the neck by pressing with both thumbs on the back of the skull and rolling the skin towards you, and over the skull, with the fingers.

Preparing the study skin (1)

I am often asked: 'Why prepare study skins of birds and mammals? Why not just have a well-mounted specimen and be done with it?' There are three main reasons. First, the specimens are needed for scientific research, to study age and geographical variation and moults. A series of specimens made up in the same way facilitates direct comparison of birds collected in different regions and at different times of the year. Secondly, study skins are much more easily handled than mounted specimens. Thirdly, there is the factor of storage economy. Imagine trying to store six mounted herons or four mounted foxes. Skins have few protrusions and can be laid alongside one another in a drawer or cabinet, taking up relatively little space.

Preparing the study skin is the next stage after skinning. Once skinning has been mastered, the practice of preparing a study skin can begin. As already mentioned, a bird or mammal skin is of little use scientifically without its full data. When your specimen has been thoroughly cleaned and preserved, it is ready to be made into a cabinet skin.

For our first attempt, we should choose a specimen of a reasonable size for easy handling. For this purpose our specimen will be the jay.

Lay the clean and preserved skin on your working surface in the same way as described for skinning – head to the left, tail to the right. Start by preparing some finely chopped tow and getting together the few tools required for the job – a pair of scissors, a pair of round-ended forceps, a mounted needle, twine, cotton-wool, needle and cotton.

Get into the routine of preparing your skin in the same way every time. Starting with the head and using the forceps, push up the neck and place two pieces of cotton-wool into the eye-sockets, one in each eye. Then, using the forceps again, take some chopped tow and place it on top of the skull between the skull and the skin. To do this successfully, take hold of the bird's beak and lift the specimen from the table.

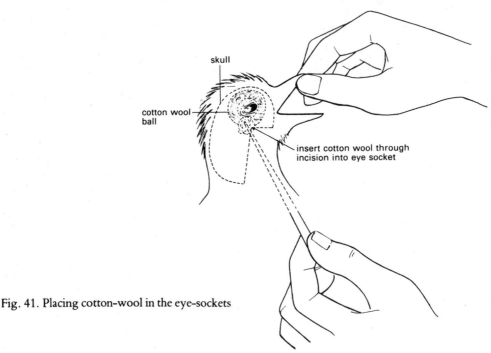

Fig. 41. Placing cotton-wool in the eye-sockets

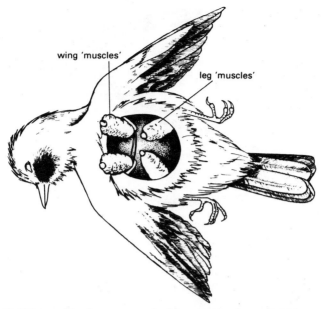

Fig. 42. Wing and leg bones wound with tow; wing bones linked together

Now push the tow and forceps up the neck and on to the top of the skull. When the top of the skull has been reached the specimen can be laid back on the table with the tow left in position. More chopped tow can be put into the cranium and around the back of the skull.

Next we turn to the wings. Finely chopped tow can be put between the radius and ulna (forearm). Tow can now be wound around the humerus (upper-arm) to replace the muscle. Pay particular attention to the shaping of this muscle, making it thin near the joint with the radius and ulna, and thicker towards the end of the bone. After preparing both wings in a similar way, link them together to prevent them floating around when the skin is made up, thus helping to control the wings and place them in their natural position.

Tie strong twine at the bottom of the humerus, near the joint with the radius and ulna. A second series of knots must now be tied, which forms a spacer, before completing the task and tying the twine to the humerus of the other wing. The space between the wings is determined by the thickness of the body. Tying the wings in this manner holds them more or less in their natural position. Finely chopped tow can be placed between the wing bones, and indeed tow can cover the whole of the back skin.

The leg bones are wrapped in the same way as the wing bones but are not tied together (see Fig. 42).

The artificial body is now prepared for the skin. The body can either be supported on a piece of dowel or, in the case of wildfowl and herons, galvanised wire, which can be bent in order to shorten the finished specimen. To find what length of dowel is required, the skin is laid out on the table in a natural position. But beware! An empty skin can be stretched beyond all proportion, so every effort must be made to ensure that the neck is not too long.

Place the dowel on the skin with the point of the dowel at the tip of the bill. The other end should just protrude beyond the tail. This ensures that the specimen, especially with passerines, can be handled simply by holding the dowel and not the actual specimen.

Having determined the length of the dowel, the neck and body can be added to the dowel. Always make the false body smaller than the real body. This will ensure that finely chopped tow can be placed round the body, and a more even shape will be achieved.

51

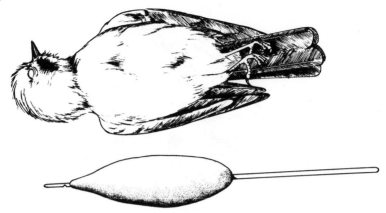

Fig. 43. Cleaned skin and artificial body before insertion

Tow is used to form the necks and bodies of small birds, but soft wood-wool is used for larger birds. At the bill end of the dowel a tapered point is made and a small notch is cut a short distance from the point. The tapered point will allow the two mandibles to close properly, and the notch will prevent the cotton from slipping when the dowel is securely tied to the bill (the upper mandible).

Both the neck and the body can be bound with twine or cotton. The dowel, when securely tied to the upper mandible, should not twist within the skin. The false body completed, it is now ready to be inserted into the skin. Gently push the neck into its position within the skin and secure the dowel to the upper mandible. This is done by passing the needle through the hard palate of the upper mandible from one side to the other. The twine is then

dowel attached
to upper mandible

Fig. 44. Attaching the dowel to the upper mandible

pulled through within the upper mandible and tied firmly into the notch on the dowel.

The rest of the skin can now be fitted properly round the body, making sure that the wings are pulled back in their natural position. The feathers on the shoulder and flank should cover the wing-butt and the leading edge of the primaries. If not, further manipulation will be necessary.

The whole skin can be picked up and turned over to make sure that the feathers of the back are lying correctly. Placing the specimen back on the table, pad the breast and flanks with finely chopped tow. When you are satisfied that the skin is full enough, sew the incision together. Care must be taken not to pull the thread too tightly, or indentations will occur along the flanks.

The cotton or twine should be waxed before use. This is done by pulling the twine over a block of beeswax. Do this two or three times, to ensure good wax impregnation.

Before our study skin is complete, we must finish the head. Chopped tow should be used to fill out the cheeks and the throat, after which the lower mandible can be sewn into place. The needle, in this case, can be pushed through the fleshy part of the lower mandible, up through the hard palate of the upper mandible and out through a nostril. Return the needle through the same nostril, but make a second hole in the hard palate down through a hole in the lower mandible which should be alongside the first hole. A

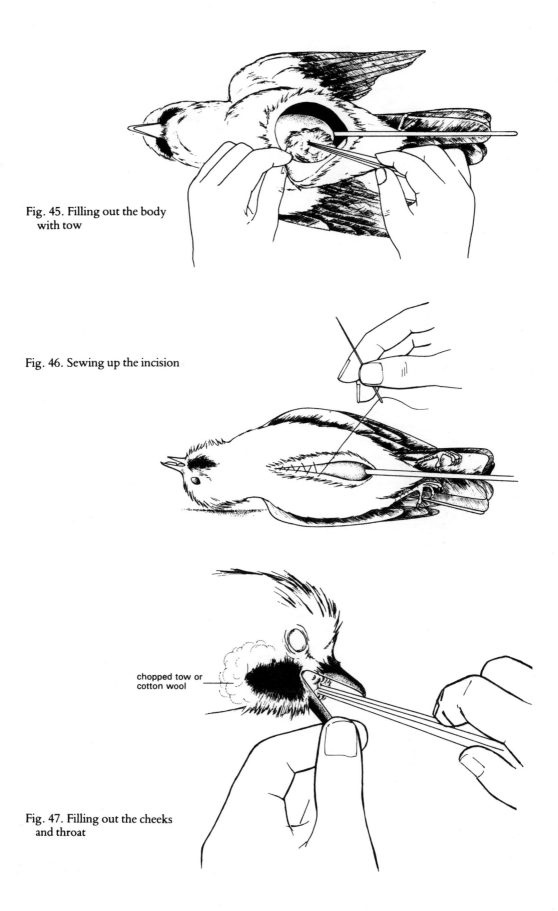

Fig. 45. Filling out the body
with tow

Fig. 46. Sewing up the incision

chopped tow or
cotton wool

Fig. 47. Filling out the cheeks
and throat

1. COTTON WOOL

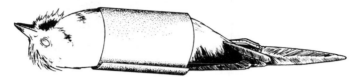

2. CARDBOARD ROLL

Fig. 48. Two ways to wrap the specimen

knot is tied, thus securing both mandibles firmly together.

The plumage of the specimen can now be rearranged and the wings fitted into their natural positions. The specimen can either have a paper tube made to fit over it, or it can be wrapped in cotton-wool or slipped into a nylon stocking.

Wrapping the specimen in a fine slither of cotton-wool is also very satisfactory and is mainly used for small delicate passerines.

The tail should be carded, and the label firmly attached. Place the specimen in a dust-proof cabinet until thoroughly dry.

There are a number of aims to achieve. The skin must be removed without too much delay for the thinner skins of birds and small mammals tend to dry quite quickly. If drying occurs, the preparator must relax the dry areas, or subsequent modelling cannot be achieved. The skin must also be removed with the minimum of disturbance to the plumage or fur. Stretching of the skin can be a problem, especially with the necks of birds and mammals, making it very difficult to loose the extra skin when modelling. After skinning is completed, the next aim is to ensure that no flesh or fat is left adhering to the skin. If any remains decomposition could occur, or, if the preservative has preserved the flesh, there will be shrinkage in that area.

After skinning, cleaning and preserving have been carried out, the task of giving the specimen a good outward appearance, a natural shape and a pleasing attitude are the remaining aims of the preparator.

ALTERNATIVE SKINNING METHODS

For birds that have large heads and narrow necks, e.g. woodpeckers, flamingos, ducks and geese, the following method is used:

Skin as normal up to the point where the head prevents the skin from continuing. Detach the neck as near to the skull as possible and remove the main body bulk. Turning the skin right-side out, an incision can be made on the crown of the head, just large enough to allow the skull and the remainder of the neck to be skinned out. After detaching the ears and skinning past the eyes, the skull can be cleaned in the normal manner.

The incision on the crown can be carefully sewn together after cotton-wool has been inserted into the eye-sockets. Chopped tow can be placed between the head skin and the skull, via the neck, later. Birds with combs should have the opening incision made under the throat.

Birds with white bellies should be skinned in one of two ways: with an incision in the back between the scapulae, or under one of the wings. In both cases the incision is well covered.

54

Fig. 49. Crown incision

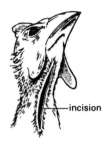

Fig. 50. Under-throat incision

The reason for these alternatives is that if the slightest amount of fat is left on the skin, it could in time leak through the incision. On a specimen with white plumage, this leakage will be visible. But if the incision is under the wing or between the scapulae, any leakage will be adequately covered. This, however, is not an excuse for leaving fat on the skin, which should be cleaned thoroughly.

Under-wing incision

This method of skinning can be used for most birds, but is usually employed when preparing the skins of small passerines. Cabinet skins prepared in this way do not require the incision to be sewn together because it is covered by the closed wing. The under-wing incision is also useful when preparing birds with white bellies such as gulls, auks and some ducks.

Place absorbent cotton-wool into the gape and vent. The initial incision is made under the wing.

Place the relaxed bird on its side with its head on the left. Lift the bird's wing and part the feathers of the back and the flank, exposing the side of the body. This process can be assisted by gently blowing on the feathers. With the sharp scalpel, make a longitudinal cut from just below the humerus, or upper-arm bone, to just in

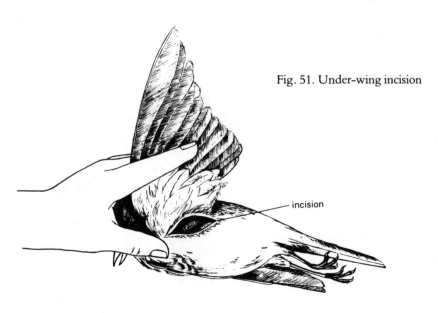

Fig. 51. Under-wing incision

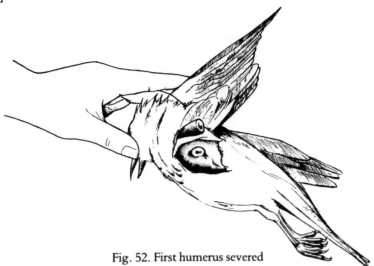

Fig. 52. First humerus severed

front of the knee-joint. With the fingers, loosen the skin all round the incision and as far back as possible on all sides. This will help to prevent it from stretching and tearing when releasing the wings and legs. Dust the opening periodically to prevent the feathers from sticking.

The humerus of the upper wing is now exposed and can easily be severed from the body. Using the fingers, continue to loosen the skin, working from over the shoulder towards the neck, which will shortly come into view.

Care should be taken to free the skin all round the neck, so that it can be cut through without fear of cutting the skin.

Dust on absorbent powder freely, and continue towards the other shoulder, loosening the skin on all sides as you go. Having exposed the other humerus, sever and release it from the body.

Taking hold of the body in one hand, you can free the skin with the other hand and make progress towards the tail. Never tug or pull strongly at any part of the skin. Speed and efficiency largely depend upon the proper use of the fingertips where the skin and flesh meet. Usually the small muscles which are attached to the skin locally may be pinched apart with the fingernails. As a matter of fact, there are few stages in the skinning procedure of

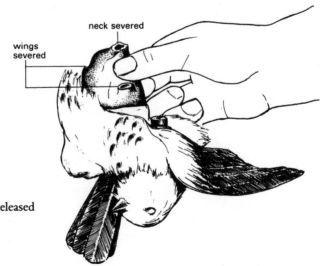

neck severed

wings severed

Fig. 53. Both wings and neck released

most birds where you need to use the scalpel blade. Ducks, cormorants and certain other water species are the exceptions, because their skins are quite firmly attached to the flesh.

The two knee-joints of the legs are soon exposed and can be cut through so that they are freed from the body. Take care when cutting through the vent. Cutting too near the skin can cut off the ventral opening, and cutting too near the body may result in the body fluids being released. The tail is the last to be disconnected from the body. As described in the ventral incision method, every effort must be made to ensure that the ends of the tail feathers are not severed.

The body is now free, and should be placed on one side until required. The head is skinned, as already described, in the ventral incision method. When it is skinned and cleaned, the wings, legs and tail can be cleaned. Finally, the inside of the skin is freed of all flesh and fat. After the plumage is cleaned and dried, the whole skin can be preserved.

Preparing the study skin (2)

The clean and preserved skin should now be turned skin-side out in order to replace the muscles of the humerus and tibia and fibula. This is done by wrapping the appropriate bone with tow or cotton-wool. Instead of tying the two humeri together as described on p. 51, a stitch is put through the two parallel feather tracts which lie below the scapular feathers. This stitch is known as a scapular or Chapin stitch and is designed to hold the skin of the back and shoulders in its natural position. The distance tied between the feather tracts depends to a large degree on the species involved. For most small passerines a single thread is adequate, but for birds of crow size and above, two threads are necessary, forming a double stitch (see Fig. 69). Two balls of cotton-wool should be put in the eye-sockets and the skin turned feather-side out. Finely chopped tow should be placed on top of the skull and the head skin. This is best inserted with fine-pointed forceps, via the neck, as described on p. 61.

The body is made in a slightly different way from that described in the ventral incision method.

A good-sized porcupine quill, or sharpened length of wood, will be required on which to form the body. The forming of the body is best done by slightly dampening the quill which enables the tow to cling to the quill when it is being rolled.

Take some fine lengths of tow in one hand. With the other rotate the quill, so rolling the tow on to it. Pay special attention to the length of the body when forming it in this way. Keep pushing the vent end of the body up the quill. Roll the tow on to the quill until the required neck thickness is reached. The fine strands of tow can now be concentrated where the body itself is to be formed.

When the correct body size is reached, it can be entered into the skin, and the bill temporarily closed. Insert the pointed end of the artificial body into the neck through the wing slit, well up into the throat of the

Fig. 54. Cleaned skin and artificial body before insertion

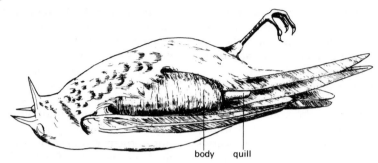

body   quill

Fig. 55. Inserting the body

specimen. Carefully manipulate the skin over the tow body by working methodically from head backwards towards the tail. To simplify matters, the whole specimen can be lifted clear of the working surface by means of the quill and by working the skin over the body with the free hand. It is important that the two humeri remain well up on the back where they are normally held in position by the scapular stitch. If the body has been made into the correct shape and size, no extra filling will be required. But extra filling, if needed, can now be put in. For the throat, this is best inserted through the open bill.

Prepare a thin piece of dowel, which is approximately one-and-a-half times the length of the specimen. Sharpen one end, and cut a notch a short distance fom the tip. Placing the thumb and finger each side of the quill at the vent end of the specimen, draw out the quill from the body by rotating it in the opposite direction to that in which the tow was rolled on. Now manipulate the skin and tuck the body

fully into place. The pointed end of the dowel is inserted through the vent itself and made to pass up the channel left by the quill. Locate the dowel by opening the bill. Put a stitch through the upper mandible (see p. 52), securing the dowel in position.

The bill can now be permanently secured. The legs should be pushed into the skin at their upper ends, crossed and tied securely to the dowel.

All that remains is to fit the wings into their natural positions, being covered by the flank feathers. As mentioned, there is no need to stitch the incision.

WRAPPING AND DRYING STUDY SKINS

After arranging the plumage of the specimen, it is necessary to wrap it while it dries. Methods of wrapping vary considerably from species to species. A thin sheet of cotton-wool is used for small passerines. Ladies' nylon stockings or

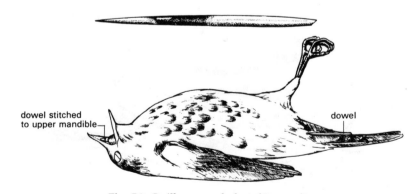

dowel stitched to upper mandible

dowel

Fig. 56. Quill removed, dowel inserted

tights are excellent for duck and goose skins. Tubes of thin card, held together with paper clips, are good for crows and game birds.

The first method mentioned above is carried out as follows: take a thin triangular piece of cotton-wool and lay it on the working surface with the apex away from you. Lay the specimen on the cotton-wool with its head in the apex. The two corners can now be brought across so that they overlap on the throat and breast. This holds the wings and flanks firmly in position. Check the position of wings and feet once more and spread the tail feathers slightly. Finally, ensure that the data label for that particular specimen remains with the skin.

The freshly prepared skins should be dried in a cupboard which has freely circulating air. This permits an even, gradual drying, eliminating drastic shrinkage.

RELAXING OLD SKINS

It may be necessary to relax the skin of a bird or mammal, either to reduce it from a mount into a study skin or vice versa. This is a difficult operation and one which can on occasion result in total disintegration of the specimen.

First method

Re-enter the specimen, cutting through the stitches of the incision, and remove as much filling as possible. If the specimen is mounted, the leg wires inside the skin will need to be cut. These can be removed by pulling the wire from the sole of the foot if the skin is sufficiently relaxed. Fill the now empty specimen with damp cotton-wool and place in a damp muslin bag. With some larger birds you will have to wrap both feet of the specimen with wet cotton-wool. The specimen is now ready to be placed in the relaxing box. Leave it until it is sufficiently relaxed.

The skin should be pulled inside out and the feather, or fur, tracts brushed gently with a fine wire brush. Carefully brush and scrape the skin all over, especially the head and neck-skin. The tail is another area that requires wire brushing. When you feel that the skin is sufficiently supple, brush on the soap-based preservative liberally, finally dusting with sawdust.

Turn the skin right-side out and go through the washing procedure. The skin is now ready to be put into its new position. Remember that the drying time for this now relaxed skin is much quicker than for a freshly processed one and no time should be wasted in the making up or modelling of the specimen.

Second method

The specimen to be relaxed is submerged in warm water. After a short time the stitches can be cut and as much of the body-filling removed as possible. After a further soaking, all filling in the body, neck and head will come away quite easily. If there are leg wires present, these are best cut off as close to the body as possible, straightened and pulled out from the inside. Twisting and turning the wire will help an easy extraction. When the body-filling and all wires have been removed, the skin can be inverted and the feather tracts gently scraped, the warm water being allowed to penetrate. When the skin is fairly supple, turn feather-side out and dry as described above after cleaning (see p. 22). Having dried the feathers, invert the skin again and liberally apply the soap-based preservative. Finally, contain the preservative with fine sawdust. After a short time the soap-based preservative will have penetrated the skin, leaving it supple.

Relaxing boxes

Depending on how often one relaxes specimens and what size they are likely to be, relaxing boxes should be as follows:

Polythene boxes can be used for the smaller specimens, but for more general purposes a wooden box, 30 in. × 24 in. × 18 in. will be found adequate. The box must be lined with a half-inch wall of plaster of Paris. To help the plaster stick to the sides of the box, small nails can be driven into wire netting on the wood, thus forming a good key. When the plaster is dry, damp sawdust can be put into the box;

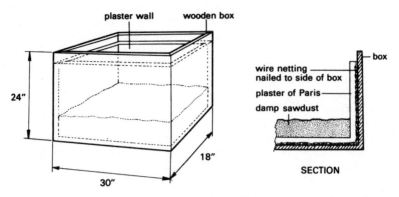

Fig. 57. Diagram of a relaxing box

there should be sufficient sawdust to allow a depth of eighteen inches. Add to the sawdust a small quantity of thymol, which will prevent mould forming in the damp atmosphere. Specimens to be relaxed can be buried in the sawdust and checked daily. Cover the top of the sawdust with a sheet of newspaper and replace the tight-fitting lid. This particular type of relaxing box was invented by a French taxidermist in the nineteenth century.

Smaller specimens can be dealt with as follows: A false bottom some 2 in. high must be placed into a polythene box large enough to accommodate the specimen, under which water to the level of 1½ in. should be added. Remove as much filling from the old specimen as possible and place the empty skin onto the false bottom. Cover with the tightly fitting lid and leave. Check the progress of the skin daily until the required condition is reached.

10

Mounting Birds

The successful mounting of birds is most certainly an art, and cannot be achieved unless the preparator has a good knowledge of his subject and a great deal of artistic ability. Every opportunity must be taken to observe birds in their own environment, whether they be small passerines around the bird table or a single wader on a river estuary. Much thought must go into the task of mounting before the actual work begins. It is important for the taxidermist to have a mental picture of the attitude of the finished specimen, since in this way the specimen can be dealt with more easily stage by stage.

The empty skin lying before you should have been preserved. It should be clean, and the feathers should lie neat and smooth. The skin should be prepared before making the artificial body. First, two small balls of cotton-wool are made and placed into each eye-socket. Secondly, some tow is chopped finely and placed on top of the skull, between the skull and the head skin. The cranium and base of the skull are filled with more chopped tow. The filling of the head is done by pushing the materials up the neck-skin with the aid of forceps.

The next job is to prevent the wings from spreading while the final mounting is being done. This is achieved by tying the two humeri together and holding them in their natural position as already described when preparing a study skin.

Replace the muscle of the two humeri with tow. Then tie a piece of strong thread at the bottom of one humerus, near the point of the humerus and radius and ulna. The two ends of the cotton are tied again some distance from the first humerus (in fact, this distance must be the correct width of the body of the specimen to be

mounted). The two ends of the cotton should now be tied round the remaining humerus, so completing the job and holding the two wings in place.

Finely chopped tow should be placed between the humeri, and in the whole of the back skin as far as the root of the tail. Next, cut four wires, two for the legs, one for the neck and one for the tail. This wire must be sufficiently strong to support the specimen when mounted, and all four wires must have a sharp point at one end. Now is the time to make the artificial body for the specimen, and there are three main points to consider: the body must be a good shape, it must be firm enough to hold the wires securely, and it must be slightly smaller than the original body. All should go well, if these points are kept in mind.

Very fine wood-wool, the sort used in the packaging of delicate fruits, should be used for the body. Take enough for the job and roll it into shape. Bind the wood-wool with cotton or twine to form the body. By placing the wood-wool body alongside the real one, an accurate model can be made.

It is sometimes necessary to stitch indentations into the body, especially at the shoulder, to allow the humeri to lie naturally. A mark, in paint or ink, should be made on the body, indicating the leg position. The neck wire can now be put into the body and secured in place. This is best done by pushing the sharpened end of the wire through the body where the neck is to be, bending the wire and pulling it back through the body, and then clenching it over. The neck can now be formed on this wire, and it can be made up of various materials such as tow, wood-wool or cotton-wool; much depends on the species being prepared. I generally tend to use fine wood-wool for birds the size of blackbird

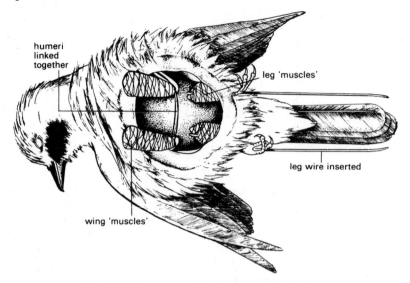

humeri
linked
together

leg 'muscles'

leg wire inserted

wing 'muscles'

Fig. 58. Skin prepared for insertion of the body

and above, tow for smaller passerines, and cotton-wool for goldcrests, wrens and humming-birds. When using wood-wool the neck can be formed by rolling the wood-wool between the hands, binding it with cotton and then fitting it on to the wire. While on an expedition to the Faroe Islands I watched an old taxidermist, Neils Abotni, form a bird's neck by rolling up small balls of tow and placing them on the wire until they reached the required length. This method proved to be extremely effective and it made the bending of the neck that much easier.

The completed body and neck are now ready to be placed into the skin. The neck can be secured into the skin in one of two ways. A point is put on the neck wire and the wire is pushed up through the skull,

coming out on the crown or through the mouth. One method is as good as the other; it is merely a case of preference.

For the purpose of this book our method will be the former – that is, pushing the neck wire up the neck and locating the exact centre of the cranium. The neck wire can now be pushed through the skull. The skull should be pushed down until the neck itself is almost in the cranium. Opening the belly skin, the body can be eased inside, the wings being pulled down the skin, so that they lie in the depressions provided. The tail can be pulled gently down, allowing the body to lie completely within the skin.

Take hold of the body with one hand and lift it from the working surface. Now check the back of the skin to see that the whole area is flat and neat. If all is well,

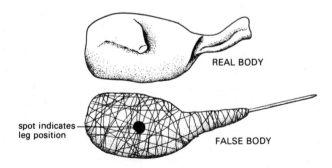

REAL BODY

spot indicates
leg position

FALSE BODY

Fig. 59. Real body and artificial body

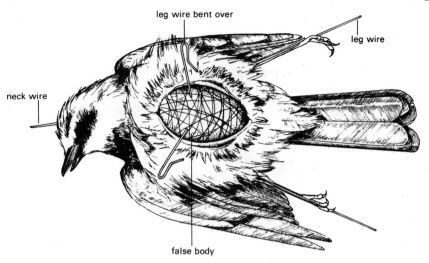

Fig. 60. Leg wires secured to the artificial body

replace the specimen. We are now ready to insert the leg wires. Taking hold of the foot in one hand and the wire in the other, pass the wire through the pad of the foot and up the back of the tarsus. The wire should pass at the back of the first joint and out, inside the skin. Turn the leg inside out and grasp the wire, pulling it through just to the length of the tibia and fibula. Tow can be wrapped around the bone and the wire to replace the muscle. The other leg is treated similarly (see Fig. 58).

Large birds, such as swans and herons, should have the tendons of the legs withdrawn in order to facilitate the insertion of strong supporting wires (see Chapter 4). If the specimen is to be set up in a walking position, in which case the ball of one foot must be clear of the ground, the wire should be pushed up the middle toe, entering it halfway down its length.

We have now reached the stage where the legs are to be secured to the artificial body. The wire of the leg should pass directly through the painted marks on the body indicating leg positions. Pass the wire right through, with sufficient length to return through the body, bend the wire, pull it back through the body and clench over the remaining end. Do exactly the same to the other leg.

The positioning of the legs is one of the most important parts of setting up birds.

Beginners tend to fit the legs too far back, making the bird appear off balance. It is much better to position the legs too far forward than too far back. But, if the leg position is marked on the artificial body beforehand, this problem should be eradicated. The legs when secured in position should be bent into the approximate attitude that they will occupy when the specimen is completed. To hold the tail in position, the previously sharpened wire can be introduced from the underside of the tail, through the root and into the body. Care must be taken not to split the quills too finely or the feathers of the tail will twist and lie incorrectly.

If the body has been made smaller than the original body of the bird, plenty of room is allowed between the body and the skin for finely chopped tow which will fill out the form to capacity. When you are satisfied that the specimen is evenly filled, the skin can be sewn together, making sure that no feathers are trapped under the thread. The specimen is now ready to be put on the temporary base or perch.

An old cake stand, used for icing cakes, makes an excellent turntable base. A flat piece of wood, with many holes drilled into its surface, should be screwed to the turntable. This is ideal for easy access to half-mounted specimens. For perching birds, twigs and branches with holes

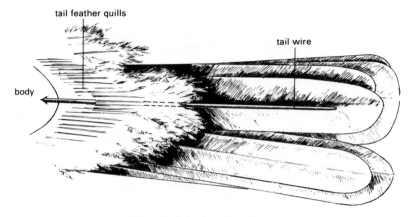

Fig. 61. Inserting the tail wire

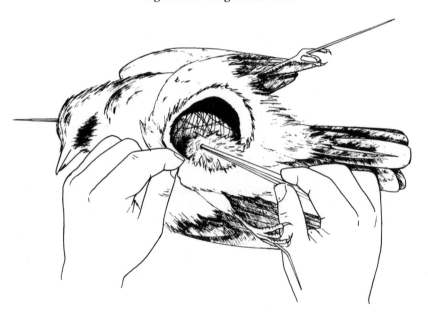

Fig. 62. Filling out the body with tow

drilled along their length make good temporary perches. These can be placed into a swivel vice, allowing the specimen to be seen from all angles. Secure the specimen to its perch.

So far, the work on our specimen has been purely mechanical, but from now until completion the taxidermist's artistic ability is tested. Bend the legs into their required position. The head and neck come next. These should be bent straight down by placing the fingers on the base of the neck close to where it joins the body. The head can now be lifted. This gives the

first bend of the neck. The second bend is made close to the skull so giving the specimen its required attitude. Securing the wings is the next task. These should be positioned at the sides of the body. On careful observation, the places where they fit will be clearly seen. Short, sharp wires are used to fasten the wings into position. The feathers of the flanks are drawn over the leading edge of the wings. Pay particular attention to the wing tips and make sure that the primaries of each wing lie together and that they are the correct distance from the end of the tail for that particular species. Lastly, position the tail. If some of the body feathers are disarranged, simply pick them up with bullnosed forceps or with the fingers and allow them to fall back into place so that they assume their natural positions.

The most important aspect of the mounted specimen is the head, and this must now be tackled. The cheeks and the throat should be filled out with finely chopped tow or good quality cotton-wool.

Remember that the head is the focal point of any mounted specimen. Great care must therefore be exercised when modelling it. Close the mandibles and secure them either with a stitch similar to that used when making the study skin, or simply with a touch of water-soluble glue. The mandibles must be held together until the glue dries. Your specimen has, until now, simply been a dead bird. But, with the introduction of the eyes, the bird standing on the temporary base will suddenly look very much alive. Be sure to choose the correct size and colour of eyes (see Appendix 3).

holes drilled in
perch for leg wires

Fig. 63. Specimen on a temporary base

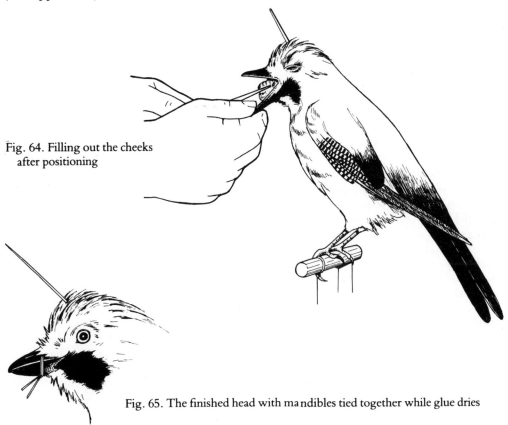

Fig. 64. Filling out the cheeks
after positioning

Fig. 65. The finished head with mandibles tied together while glue dries

65

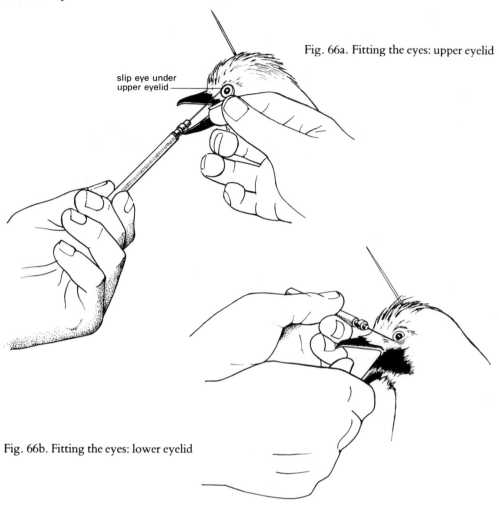

slip eye under
upper eyelid

Fig. 66a. Fitting the eyes: upper eyelid

Fig. 66b. Fitting the eyes: lower eyelid

The positioning of the eyes is not as easy as it may seem, for both eyes must be parallel and they must be looking in the same direction. Many are the times I have left my studio in angry frustration at the difficulty of getting the eyes to look natural. If you decide to put them in while the specimen is still fresh and the orbits are still supple, bear in mind that a certain amount of shrinkage will occur. To compensate for this, close the eyelids a little more than is necessary, because when shrinkage occurs the eyes will open a little wider. If you fail to compensate in this way, the dry eyes will have a staring effect.

Many preparators leave the eye-fixing until the specimen is dry. In this way maximum shrinkage has already taken place, and to fit the eyes damp cotton-wool is placed in the eye-sockets and the lids are relaxed. The eyes can now be fitted and held in place with a touch of glue.

The toes should be pinned to the temporary perch. Never neglect this feature in birds, as there is nothing worse than seeing a bird which is not gripping its perch. Two pieces of card are used to sandwich the feathers of the tail together and paperclips hold these in position. A securing pin is passed from one side of the cards to the other which will hold the tail in its natural contour.

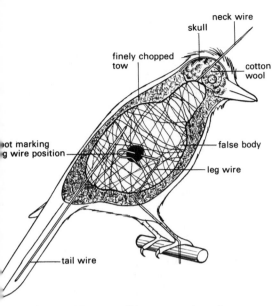

neck wire
skull
finely chopped tow
cotton wool
ot marking
g wire position
false body
leg wire
tail wire

Fig. 67. Diagram of the mounted specimen

BINDING

Binding the specimen is an essential part of the mounting of birds. The binding is used to hold stubborn feathers in their natural position until the skin is dry. In making study skins, specimens are wrapped in cotton-wool or placed in a nylon stocking (see pp. 58-9). These materials are not always practical when mounting birds, however. It may be found that feathers are protruding in various places. If so, insert short sharpened wires, with an s-bend on one end, into the specimen, usually in the mid-line position, and wrap soft cotton or wool around the specimen and over the loops of the wire. These loops act as a type of scaffolding, keeping the cotton away from the areas where it is not required. If, for instance, only one area has stubborn feathers – either the breast or the rump – then all that is required is a square piece of card, with a pin through it, placed over the affected area and fixed securely to the body, so that the feathers are held down. After being wrapped and finally adjusted, the specimen can be put away in a dust-free place until it is thoroughly dry. The painting of the soft parts and the fixing of the specimen to its display perch will complete

this highly skilled task of setting up a bird.

When mounting specimens which have lax dorsal plumes, such as egrets and birds of paradise, in a displaying attitude, it is essential that the plumes be erected above the back of the specimen. As the plumes are so delicately structured, it would be impossible to suspend each individual feather. To overcome this problem, after mounting is completed suspend the specimen upside down, arrange the plumes and leave in this position until dry.

FLYING BIRDS

To show aggressive display, landing, taking off, preening and other actions, it is sometimes necessary to mount a bird in a flying position, or at least in a position where the wings are held free from the body. To do this, a wire, which is strong enough to support the wing, is passed alongside the wing bones and out close to the first, second or third primary. It may be found easier to push the wires from the inside of the wing skin, and make it re-appear beyond the primaries. The wing wires are, of course, sharpened at both

Fig. 68. Binding the specimen

ends. There is no need to tie the humeri together when wiring the wings. The wing wire is secured to the body in exactly the same way as for the leg wires. If the bird is to be in free flight, it must be supported by one of its wing wires rooted to the rock work, or branch, or to the side of its case. Birds such as ducks which are either taking off or landing, have their supporting wire protruding from the vent or side of the body. This wire is neatly camouflaged by reed, or grass, or by whichever natural setting you choose your specimen to be displayed in. After bending the wing into its required position it may be found necessary to card the secondaries and primaries. This is done by cutting two pieces of card which will cover the length of the wing. To give good coverage the card should be almost half the width of the wing. These two cards can be held in place with ordinary sewing pins and paperclips. The tail can be spread and held in a similar manner. For larger birds, a sharp thin wire should be prepared and passed through each individual tail feather until they are all threaded on to the wire. This wire should be as close to the root of the tail as possible, so that it will be hidden by the tail coverts. The tail can now be fanned to the desired position.

SCAPULAR AND RUMP STITCHES

Most bird species from blackbird size upwards should be fitted with wing wires which run the whole length of the wing. The wire is attached to the body in a similar manner to that already described for the leg wires. In this case the humeri should not be tied together, but a humeral or scapular stitch be used. This will hold the skin between the humeri in a natural position.

When you have located the two humeral tracts, push the needle through one of the tracts and pull through the waxed twine, leaving a loose end, which will ultimately be tied to the other loose end. Push the needle through the other tract directly opposite the first. Bring it across to the first feather tract, but this time at the lower end

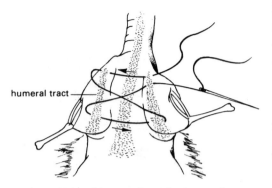

Fig. 69. Double scapular (Chapin) stitch

of the tract. Cross the body again to the lower end of the other tract and back up to the starting position, where the two loose ends can be tied together. The tighter the twine is pulled, the closer the two tracts come together, so it is quite easy to achieve the correct body distance. Finely chopped tow can now be put between the stitch and the skin forming a smooth full back.

When setting up certain game species, e.g. grouse, blackcock and pheasant, it is necessary to use a further stitch, the rump stitch. This is done in a similar way to the double scapular stitch but from the lower back to the rump. The stitches are this time placed into the femoral tracts and when completed finely chopped tow can be placed as described for the scapular stitch.

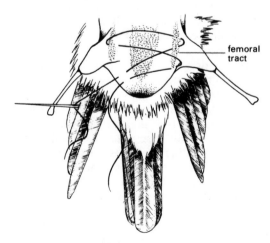

Fig. 70. Rump stitch

11

Skinning Mammals

To begin with, measure the animal. If it is to be made into a cabinet skin, collect the relevant data, or the more intricate measurements if the specimen is to be mounted (see p. 84 for measuring large mammals).

VENTRAL INCISION

Lay the specimen on the working surface with its belly uppermost. Part the fur of the belly and make a cut from the lower end of the rib cage to a point between the hind legs. If the specimen is a male, cut to one side of the genitals. The incision should be straight, and care must be taken not to cut too deeply, for if the body cavity is opened, spillage of blood and bowel will occur. The skin should now be freed along one side of the body, which is best done by using a dull knife and cutting in a slanting action between the skin and body flesh. After freeing the skin on one side as much as possible, turn the specimen round, and proceed to loosen the skin on the other side. The dull knife is a great help for this job if used as described, as it is quite difficult to make the cutting edge penetrate the skin. I find fine hardwood sawdust is the best absorbent to use when skinning any of the larger mammals.

One of the legs must now be disarticulated. The knee-joint is pushed up through the incision and cut (Fig. 72). The beginner should include all the leg bones when mounting the specimen, so the femur should be released from the pelvic girdle (Fig. 73), cleaned and set aside to be fixed to the tibia and fibula later. Release the other leg in the same way; retain and clean the femur. Next, cut through the vent of the animal and all around the hindquarters, exposing the root of the tail. Mammal skinning is not as pleasant as bird skinning, nor is it such a delicate operation, so the taxidermist must not be afraid of handling the mammal specimen. Skin along the length of the exposed root of the tail as far as possible towards the tip. Loosen the skin along the back of the animal in readiness to slip the tail vertebrae from the skin. This is best done by placing the specimen's tail into the tail block, which is a piece of wood five inches wide and ten inches long, with a v-shaped cut in the top. Place the tail block in the vice, drop the exposed root of the tail into the v-shaped cut and pull against the tail skin, slipping the vertebrae out and freeing the skin from the rear end of the specimen. In small specimens the vertebrae can be pulled out quite easily with the fingers.

The carcass can now be suspended from a pulley or hooks. I prefer to place a noose around the rear end of the body, just in front of the legs, and hoist the specimen to the required height. Both hands can now be used in freeing the skin from the body. By skinning carefully, most of the flesh and fat can be left adhering to the body, making the cleaning of the skin easier; remember to turn the carcass constantly to ensure that it is skinned evenly. Smaller specimens such as the squirrel are easily skinned without being suspended.

On reaching the shoulders, care must be taken not to hole the skin, for you will find that skin around the chest and in the pits of the front limbs fits very tightly. Having released the chest, skin all around the back and shoulders until the humerus, or upper-arm, appears, showing the articulation of the shoulder joint. Continue to skin down the front limb until the joint with the fore-arm appears. Now the fore-limb can be released from the shoulder joint. Repeat the

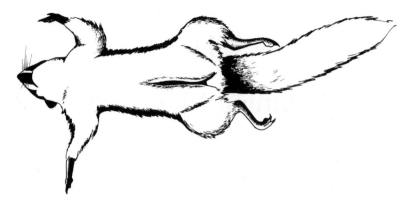

Fig. 71. First ventral incision

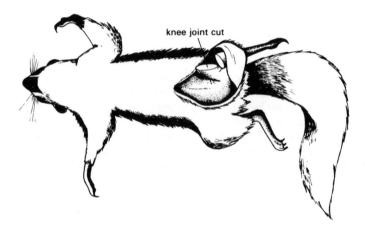

Fig. 72. Leg exposed and knee–joint cut

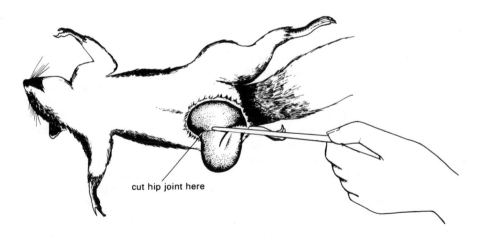

Fig. 73. Releasing the leg at hip–joint

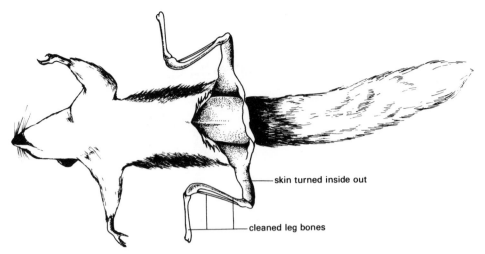

Fig. 74. Leg bones exposed and cleaned

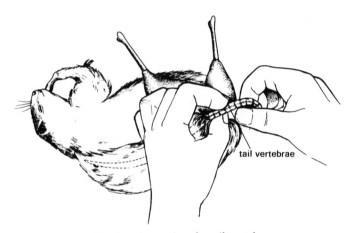

Fig. 75. Extracting the tail vertebrae

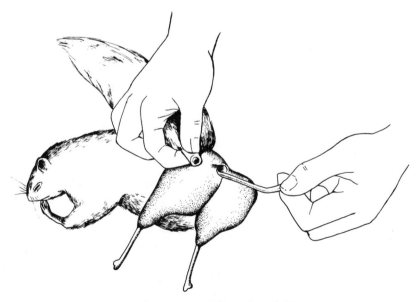

Fig. 76. Vertebrae extracted from the tail skin

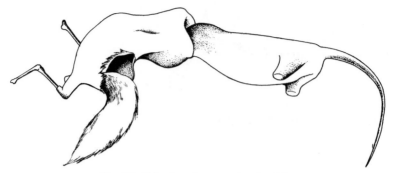

Fig. 77. Skinning down to the shoulders

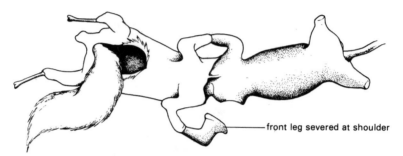

front leg severed at shoulder

Fig. 78. Front leg exposed and cut at the shoulder

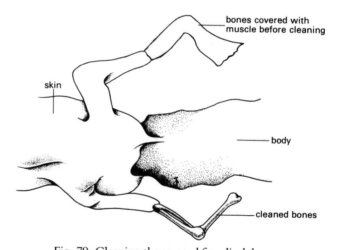

bones covered with
muscle before cleaning

skin

body

cleaned bones

Fig. 79. Cleaning the severed fore-limb bones

same procedure with the other front leg.

At this stage the suspended carcass will need to be hoisted up a notch or two, bringing the head into a comfortable working position. Skin down the neck to the base of the skull. Here you will see two cartilaginous bulges. These are the ears, which must be cut with care. Take hold of one, and with the thumb and fingers feel for the narrow tube at the very root. This can be cut through, thus freeing the ear. Having released both ears, continue to skin the top of the head and the sides of the face. Take great care here, for to make a hole in the head skin would be disastrous, especially around the eyes.

I might just mention at this point that a box or table placed under the skin will

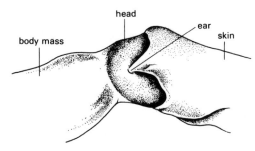

Fig. 80. Head skinned down to the ears

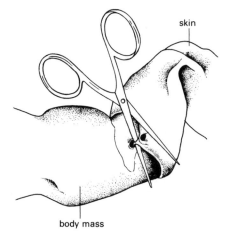

Fig. 81. Roots of ears cut close to the skull

support it and prevent it from stretching. Placing the hand up inside the skin and pushing the finger into, and between, the eyelids will help in locating the eyes. The skin round the eyes can now be cut without too much difficulty. Skin down the muzzle towards the nose and also under the lower jaw, keeping as close to the skull as possible. Cut through the mouth membrane, beginning at the side of the mouth.

Having made the cut, insert a finger and, applying tension to this skin, cut close to the teeth along the lower and upper jaws. Turn the carcass round and repeat the process on the other side, finally freeing the skin from the lower jaw and the cartilage of the nose. When the skinning is completed, remove the carcass and place on one side until required for modelling the artificial body.

Cleaning the skin

Before removing the muscle from each limb, remember to make a touch drawing to help when mounting the specimen later.

Taking each limb in turn, pull it inside out as far as the carpal joint, removing all

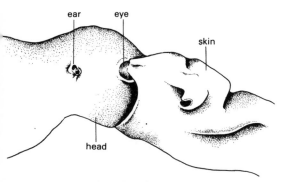

Fig. 82. Head ready to be skinned round the eye

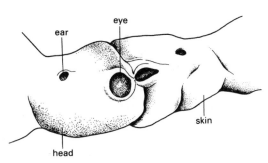

Fig. 83. Cutting the skin round the eye

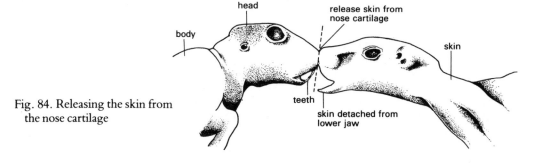

Fig. 84. Releasing the skin from the nose cartilage

73

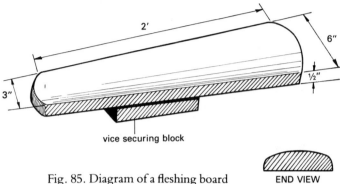

Fig. 85. Diagram of a fleshing board   END VIEW

the flesh from the limb bones. Repeat on the hind legs, being sure to remove all fat and flesh from the bones. Next, turn your attention to the head skin. Thoroughly clean the roots of the ears and, having done this, split the outer skin from the cartilage of the ear, leaving an opening for the filling, which will add rigidity when modelling takes place. The skin round the eyes must be split also and so too must the lips. This is done by cutting between the outer and inner skin, finally leaving the area clean and free to take the filling which will ultimately form the lip. Take care not to cut through the roots of the whiskers or they will fall out. The flesh and fat must now be removed from the whole of the skin, paying particular attention to the edges of the incision. Remember that if any fat or flesh is overlooked, the area may decompose, a fatty deposit may occur or the area may shrink badly, so every effort must be made to get rid of all fat and flesh.

To extract the fatty tissues from the larger areas of the skin, slip the skin flesh-side out over a fleshing board, which is a piece of wood two feet by six inches. This is held in the vice and will enable the skin to be scraped and the unwanted tissues to be removed.

Be sure to take out the thick fats from around the vent and root of the tail. When satisfied with the cleanliness of the inside of the skin, turn it the right-side out and split all four pads, making sure the skin is freed all round the carpal and tarsal joints and remove all flesh and fats. The skin is now ready to be placed in the preservative of your choice and checked daily (see

Chapter 5). The final cleaning of the skin is done when fixing has been carried out.

Preparing a study skin

The preparation of a mammal skin is very similar to that of a bird and is a mechanical process. Little or no artistic ability is required. However, the skin must be clean and neat.

After skinning, cleaning and preserving, the empty skin is laid on one side and the artificial body is prepared. A piece of galvanised wire or a dowel is cut to the exact length of the head and body. On to this is bound some fine wood-wool. The shape we are aiming to achieve is like that of a large cigar – the pointed end for the head and the rounded end for the rear. Taking the skin, bind tow onto the four limb bones replacing the natural muscles. For mammals larger than squirrel size, wires must be inserted alongside the four limb bones, as is done with mounted mammals. These can be pushed into the body at a later stage anchoring them firmly. Alternatively, a strengthening wire can be passed along the inside of the front limb, down the side of the body and along the bone of the rear limb, finally protruding through the foot. The same procedure is repeated on the opposite side of the specimen. These two parallel wires give rigidity to the four limbs without being anchored to the body form in any way.

Fit the cigar-shaped body into the skin and if necessary use supporting wires for the limbs. Finely chopped tow should be placed into areas such as the shoulders and

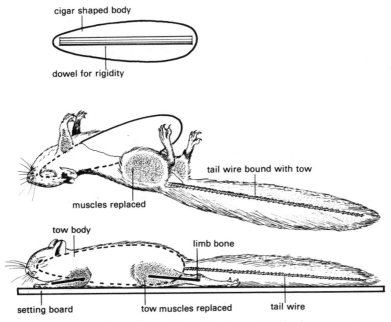

cigar shaped body

dowel for rigidity

tail wire bound with tow

muscles replaced

tow body

limb bone

setting board

tow muscles replaced

tail wire

Fig. 86. Preparing and inserting the artificial body

the base of the tail. A tail wire, wrapped with tow, or a feather quill should be pushed down the tail skin and anchored to the body. Arrange and sew the incision together neatly. A series of stitches are used to hold the mouth firmly in place.

The skin is now ready to be pinned in place on a soft wooden base until dry. The front limbs should be pinned with the palms downwards and should not pro-

trude further forward than the nose. The rear limbs are bent at the knee joint and are pinned in the same manner with the soles of the feet facing downwards.

The toes of both front and rear feet should now be evenly spread. Arrange the tail and finally lay the ears flat along the head. These may have to be held in place with pins and card.

SKINNING THROUGH THE MOUTH

The method of skinning specimens through the mouth is used for small mammals up to, and including, the size of a squirrel. This method is largely used when preparing study skins. It ensures that no incision spoils the skin on either the upper or lower surfaces. Mice, for instance, which are suckling young, are best prepared in this way, as the teats will appear undisturbed when the skin is completed. Squirrels which show moult patterns on the dorsal and ventral surfaces should also be prepared by this method.

The specimen is laid on the working surface and each side of the mouth enlarged just enough to enable the skull to

Fig. 87. Enlarging the mouth.

Fig. 88. Skinning of the skull completed

pass through the open mouth. With the scalpel, the mucous lining of the lips should be cut as close to the skull as possible. The nose cartilage should also be freed. The skin can now be peeled back as far as the eyes. Care must be taken not to cut the eyelids, as this would leave an unrepairable hole.

After successfully freeing the skin around the eyes, you must attend to the ears. These can quite easily be pulled firmly from their origin, so completing the skinning of the skull.

Holding the specimen free of the working surface by means of the head, you can pull down the skin of the neck until both forelegs are exposed. Placing the specimen back on the table, you can deal with the forelegs individually by the method described in the normal skinning process. With both fore limbs free, pull the skin down as far as it will go, exposing both

hind limbs and the root of the tail. These can now be dealt with in the normal manner and the skin cleaned and freed of all flesh and fats and then preserved.

Making up the skin

All four limb bones should be wrapped with fine tow, and the tail-wire or feather quill inserted. The skin can now be turned fur-side out. Fine hardwood sawdust, which has been dampened previously, should be put through the mouth and the skin filled to capacity. A pencil can be used to pack the sawdust in firmly. The head can be filled with a wad of cotton-wool or wood-wool, rolled to the original shape of the skull, and the lips stitched into place.

It is quite easy to end up with a skin twice as long as the original specimen. The touch drawing, which was made previously, enables one to fit the skin on to the drawing and to pin all four feet to the cork base. The specimen is then left until dry. The skull of the specimen should be prepared as described in Chapter 18. When it is completed and dry, it should be attached to the specimen, which should then be labelled and stored.

Fig. 90. Study skin, cleaned skull and label

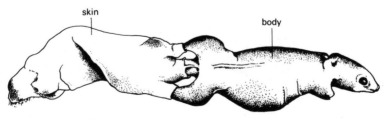

Fig. 89. Body skinned down to hind legs and root of tail

BATS

Small mammals, such as bats, are usually skinned through an incision made across the lower part of the abdomen. In this way the skin of the belly and back is not disfigured. The skin is made up by making a small body of tow, and a stitch put in the mouth and finally across the belly incision. The wings are usually dealt with by closing one naturally to the body and by extending the other.

Pins are used to hold the wing in position. Do not pin through the limbs or the membrane; otherwise holes and tears may occur. Pins strategically placed can have cotton stretched between them, holding the wing taut and in place until dry.

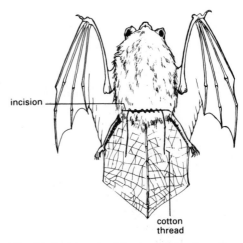

Fig. 91. Incision for skinning bats and small mammals

12

Tanning Animal Skins

The following process will be found useful for the tanning of most animal skins.

After the skin has been removed from the carcass it should be plunged into a bath of cold water to which has been added a little liquid soap; this will help remove blood and grime from the skin. If the skin has been previously salted, this bath will also remove the unwanted salt. Leave the skin submerged for three to four hours.

Salted and dried skins will require a little more attention before they are supple enough to go through the next process.

Remove them from the cold water and soap bath and put them across the fleshing beam. Using the fleshing knife, pull out all the wrinkles and creases until the skin becomes supple. This process may have to be repeated several times until the skin reverts to its natural state.

When you have washed the skins thoroughly, they are ready to be put into the pickle which, for 50 lb skins, consists of:

water (warm)	12½ gall
salt	13 lb
sulphuric acid	13½ fl oz
formic acid	11 fl oz
pancreal F.A.	2½ lb

For a lesser weight of skins, obviously the ingredients are reduced accordingly.

The pickle is made in a vessel which must be large enough to allow free movement of the skins which, by frequent rotation, will ensure that the pickle penetrates all areas. The skins are left in the pickle for a period of time which varies according to the thickness of the skins.

Most skins will be adequately impregnated within two or three days,

after which they are removed and hung over a wooden horse to drain. Skins can be safely left over the horse for about a week.

The pancreal in the skins is still active and continues to work until the skins are dry.

If you intend to use the pickled skin for mounting, all that remains to be done is to pare the skin down and give a final clean to the flesh side, removing any remaining fat or flesh. Be sure to do this before the skin becomes too dry.

It may be necessary to degrease the skin, especially if it is from a fat-bearing species such as a seal.

Place the skin into a degreasing agent such as trichlorethylene. Ideally, the skins should be constantly moving, in which case a machine similar to the cleaning drum will be required. But frequent movements – as for pickling – will be possible only when a small number of skins are being degreased. Leave the skin in a degreasing solution for twenty-four hours, after which it should be removed and allowed to drain. After washing and drying, it will be ready for mounting (see Chapter 13).

RUGS AND FLAT SKINS

To prepare either flat skins for study purposes, or rugs for daily use, more work must be done on the skin before it is sufficiently soft and clean.

The pickle already mentioned is used for skins which are of considerable thickness and which will not readily absorb the solution.

The following solution will be found suitable for skins which are considered thin and will readily absorb the solution; for 50 lb skins:

water (warm)	12½ gall
salt	12½ lb
sulphuric acid	13½ fl oz
formic acid	11 fl oz

The addition of pancreal is not necessary in this recipe.

The longer the wet skins are left over the wooden horse the softer they will ultimately become.

The skins, now ready for tanning, should be placed in a drum or container of cold water, to which is added salt and Paralene CFT, 4½ gallons per 50 lb weight of skins. The skins are left in this solution until they are fully impregnated, which usually takes between three and four days, during which time they should be rotated frequently.

Having completed this part of the tanning, add previously mixed soda bicarbonate to the water and paralene solution. This should be added at a ratio of 3 lb per 50 lb weight of skins. The soda bicarbonate is mixed into a paste with warm water and added to the tannage until a hydrometer reading of pH 4 is reached. This should be added over a period of two to three hours while the mixture is rotating, in order to ensure complete integration of the soda bicarbonate. Leave the skins in this solution overnight. The skins are then removed and placed over a wooden horse, flesh-side up, for some twenty-four hours, after which they are washed thoroughly to remove the surplus tannage and air-dried.

These processes will have had a thickening effect on the skins which is due to the absorption of the various chemicals. The skins must now be shaved to an even thickness. It is important that the skin be neither too wet nor too dry. If it is too wet, shaving will be hampered by excess water. On the other hand, if it is too dry it will not shave evenly.

Fat liquor

Having arrived at a skin of even thickness, you must now replace the natural oils of the skin and lubricate the hide fibres by immersing the skins in a solution of 1 per cent fat liquor WWL to 12½ gallons of water. The skins are left in the liquor for approximately one and a half hours.

After completing the fat liquor process, the skins should be removed from the liquor, stretched out and left in a warm room to dry. When dry, they should be draped over the wooden horse and left for one or two days to season. After seasoning, the skins should be put through a final degreasing process by washing in trichlorethylene and then dried.

To obtain a soft smooth finish, the leather side of the skin should be buffed. This can be done with the use of a sandpaper disc attached to an electric drill. Brushing and combing the hair or wool side of the skin completes the process.

13

Mounting Mammals

MOUNTING SMALL MAMMALS

For mammals up to and including fox size, the method for mounting is as follows:

A body form should be made from wood-wool, incorporating the cleaned and preserved skull, or, if available, a substitute cast.

Take a length of galvanised wire, approximately twice the length of the original body, and bend it into the shape of the body. Using damp wood-wool, bind the body incorporating the wire shape (see Fig. 92), with the completed body being as near to the original as possible. With the wires protruding from the neck, secure the original skull. The floor of the mouth and the cheeks should now be added – these are best made of fine wood-wool – and bound on to the skull with twine.

The position of the shoulders and the hips, where both front and rear limbs are attached to the body, should be marked in order to secure the limb wires in the correct position on the artificial body.

Before fitting the now clean and preserved skin on to the manikin, put it into the cleaning drum, which contains a quantity of hardwood sawdust, and drum it until the fur is dry. Shake the excess sawdust from the fur and blow out the remainder with compressed air.

The modelling compound is mixed to the consistency of putty in readiness to be spread thinly over the wood-wool body form which has been previously made. The compound is spread from the skull over the neck and shoulders, down the back and sides of the body, to the tail. The same compound is pushed between the cartilage and the outer skin of the ear before fitting.

The skin

The four limbs should now be considered. The first thing to do is to cut four supporting wires approximately twice as long as the length of each leg. The wire must be strong enough to support the standing animal on completion. Each wire should have a sharpened point at one end. Pass the point of the wire through the pad of the foot and up the inside of the skin along the limb bones. The muscles are replaced by tow or fine wood-wool.

Each limb must be checked against its touch drawing. When the tow or wood-wool has been bound on to the bone with cotton or twine, a thin layer of modelling compound is added and the limb pulled the right-side out. Make sure that the large muscle of the hind legs is firm and of a good shape.

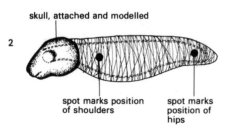

Fig. 92. Making the artificial body

80

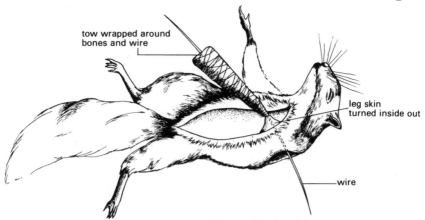

Fig. 93. Inserting the leg wires and replacing the muscles with tow

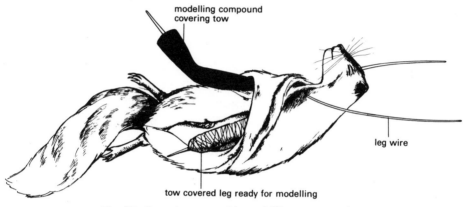

Fig. 94. Covering tow with modelling compound

Extra modelling compound can be put into the heel of the hind leg so that, when pulled right-side out, the compound can be squeezed to form the tendon of the leg.

After covering the hind limbs in the same manner as described for the fore limbs, pull them the right-side out ready for the skin to be fitted on the body form. It is important to ensure that the skin is pulled down evenly. In the initial stages, make sure that the head and neck-skin are in the correct position. The pointed wire of one of the front legs can now be pushed through the body in the place indicated by the dot in Fig. 92. As it is pushed right through, an s-bend is put on the wire, which is pulled back, locking the leg wire firmly into the body. Repeat on the other front leg. Push the bones of the legs hard up to the body and bend them down close to the side. Take the humerus, hold it still

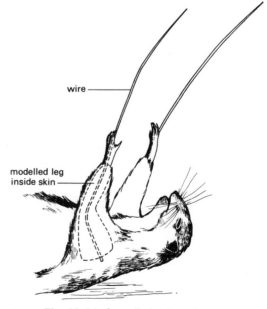

Fig. 95. Limbs pulled right-side out

81

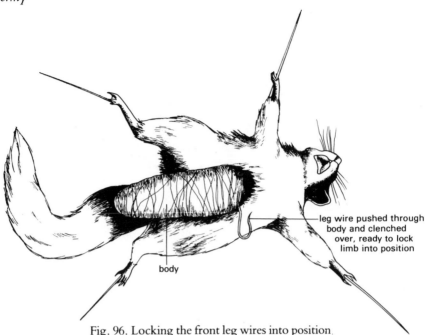

leg wire pushed through
body and clenched
over, ready to lock
limb into position

body

Fig. 96. Locking the front leg wires into position.

and bend the radius and ulna forward into the natural standing position. With both front legs done in this way, continue to push the body into the skin as far down as the hind limbs and tail. Before the hind legs are locked in their positions, insert the previously prepared tail wire. This wire should have both ends sharpened, and tow can be wound on to it. A little glue placed about three inches from one end will hold the fine tow while you wind and form the tail shape. This artificial tail insert must not be too thick or it will not go down the whole length of the tail.

Proceed to lock the hind legs into the

body in exactly the same way as described for the front limbs. Open both legs wide and, forcing them backwards and downwards, insert the end of the tail wire, pushing it right through the body so that it comes out in the belly region. Clench the tail wire over, locking it firmly into the body. Before positioning the hind legs and before sewing the skin of the belly together, you may have to fill part of the shoulders, especially where the humeri meet the body. If so, this can be done by inserting a small wad of fine wood-wool or tow which has been impregnated with modelling compound. The wad is placed

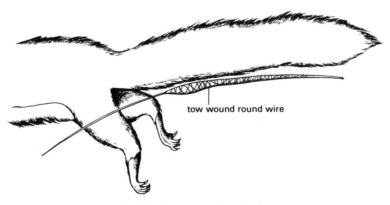

tow wound round wire

Fig. 97. Preparing the tail wire

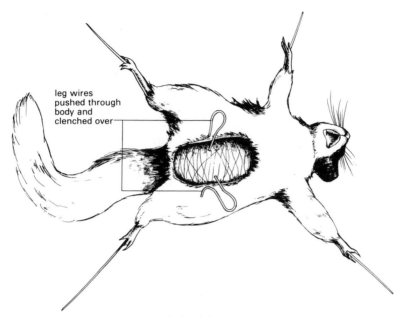

Fig. 98. Locking the back leg wires into position

leg wires
pushed through
body and
clenched over

in the depression and patted into place from the outside. Any other hollow is done in a similar way. Bend both hind legs up towards the head, hold the femur and bend the tibia and fibula back towards the tail. The lower part of the foot can be bent in the opposite direction. The specimen, partially shaped, can be placed on to its base.

The mechanical side of preparing the specimen is completed and, if this part has been carried out correctly, little effort should be needed to position the animal for it to be anatomically correct. Before actually standing the specimen on its base, fill the feet with modelling compound and sew the pads neatly together. Now stand the specimen up. Drill four holes in the base, in the positions which the feet should take, and bend the leg wires under the base, making sure that the feet are tight to the board. The toes should be spread slightly and bent to give the impression that pressure is on them. The advantage of this method is that the position of the specimen can be changed if required.

Finally the head has to be modelled and the eyes put into position. Starting with the ears, take hold of the left or right ear and squeeze the modelling compound into

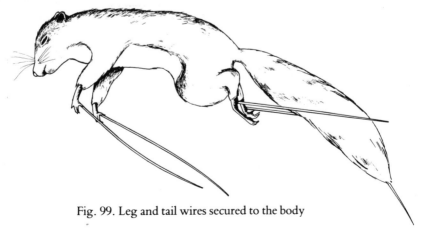

Fig. 99. Leg and tail wires secured to the body

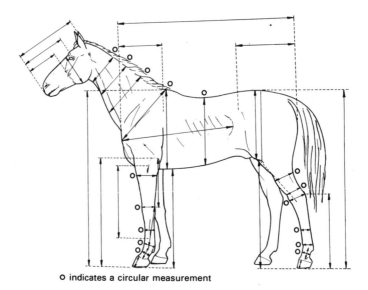

o indicates a circular measurement

Fig. 100. Measurements necessary before skinning

every part of it, making sure it reaches the tip. The tendency here is to make the ears too fat by not squeezing the compound evenly into them. The roots of the ears are equally important and the compound should be spread past the roots and on to the top of the skull to form a strong base. A wire is sharpened and pushed through the ear from tip to root and passed into the skull. Leave some wire protruding from the tip until the ear dries.

The eyes can be put into the skull before mounting, or they can be put in last. Whichever way is preferred, great care must be taken because the eyes are probably the most important feature of the mounted animal. There are three main points to remember about the eyes. First, both eyes must be parallel and looking in the same direction. Secondly, they must be pushed well into the skull; otherwise when the skin dries they will appear to bulge and stare. Thirdly, take care when painting the eyelids for very little colour is required.

The lips and nose must now be modelled. Never stitch the lips together, as this does not look natural. By splitting the mucus lining of the lips we have created an area into which we can fold a long roll of modelling compound. The inside of the lip can be folded over naturally, trapping the compound and making the lip look good

and full. Having removed all the cartilage from the nose, you can push modelling compound in, making sure that it fills the inside of the nose. With both upper and lower lips packed, and also the nose, all that remains is to fit the lower jaw skin into place and pin securely. Bring down the upper part or muzzle and pin along the underside of the lips, holding the mouth lightly shut. Two short wires can be pushed up each nostril and into the skull. These will help to hold the nose in place as well as adding strength.

MEASURING AND MOUNTING LARGE ANIMALS

Fig. 100 shows where measurements must be taken and how many, before the specimen is skinned. These measurements are necessary in the final fitting of the skin to the manikin. A second series of measurements, following the same sequence, are taken from the specimen when the skin has been removed. It is from these measurements that the artificial body or manikin is constructed.

The initial incision begins at the chest, along the median line of the belly to the tip of the tail, continues up the back of each leg from the bottom of the foot, over the centre of the large tendon in the hind leg and the elbow in the front leg, and up to the intersection of the median cut.

In short-haired animals, e.g. antelope, horse or deer in summer coat, an incision is never made up the underside of the neck unless absolutely necessary, as it is almost impossible to conceal the stitches. For horses, at least, an incision is best made along the underside of the mane. The stitches can then be concealed by the mane.

As already described, the ears of most small and large mammals should be skinned and inverted, freeing the outer skin at the back of the ear from the cartilage. Likewise, the mucus lining of the lips should also be split, and the nose cartilage removed.

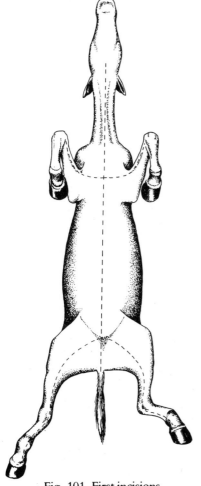

Fig. 101. First incisions

The following method was first mentioned by Hornaday in *Taxidermy and Zoological Collecting* (1891). By this method the skull and limbs were made fast to a rigid centre-board and the supporting leg wires bolted to a base-board. In those days, after building up the body and muscle structure with wood-wool, the whole manikin was covered in clay. Today the technique is much the same, but in place of clay preparators use a modelling compound.

The manikin

Fig. 102 shows how the manikin for a large-sized animal, in this case a horse, is constructed. The main shape of the body is cut out of half-inch board. The skinned body of the animal is simply laid on the board and the body shape marked with a pencil. The line which will eventually be cut out should be between half an inch and an inch smaller all round. This smaller shape will allow for the modelling compound to be modelled to the correct size, a larger body being difficult to reduce.

After the centre-board has been cut out, four blocks should be made. These are to ensure that both the front limbs and the back limbs are secured at the correct distance apart. They should now be attached to the centre-board in their correct position. The front ones should be placed where the humerus joins the scapula and the rear block should be placed where the femur joins the pelvic girdle. After securing the blocks, holes can be drilled in them to take the supporting wires.

Choose wires that will adequately support the weight of the specimen. The horse, for instance, has four leg wires of half inch soft iron. The neck wires, which support the skull, are the same as those used for the limbs. The only other permanent wire is to support the tail, and this can obviously be of a much lighter gauge.

When the wires are secured, the cleaned limb bones can be attached in their original positions, tied to the supporting wires and bent into the required attitude.

The neck wires supporting the skull can now be fitted. A regular check should be made to see that all measurements are

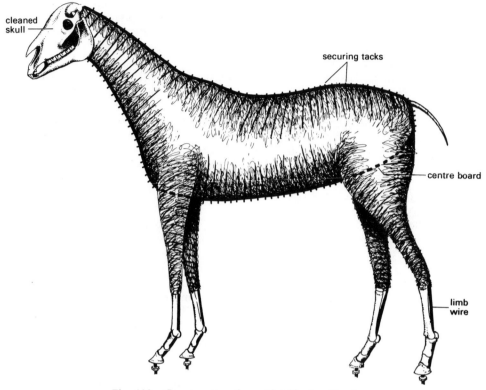

Fig. 102a. Constructing the artificial body: side view

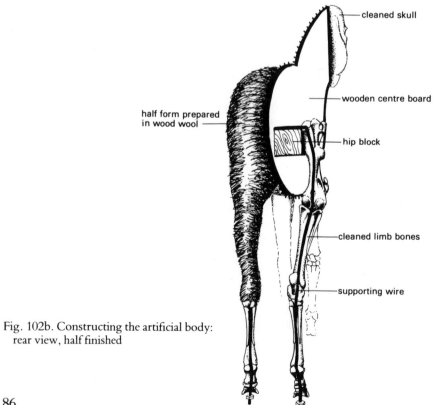

Fig. 102b. Constructing the artificial body:
rear view, half finished

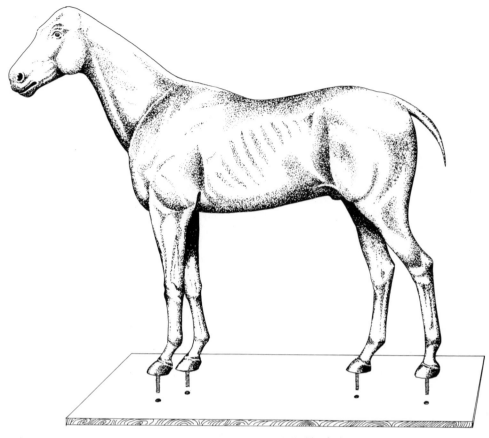

Fig. 103. Completed modelled body

correct. The base on which to secure the manikin is of the utmost importance. A flimsily built one will only frustrate matters and time will be lost rectifying the fault. Ideally, a strong base, which is at workable height, is by far the best. An area should be kept free all around the manikin so that the modelling can be viewed from all quarters.

A thread should be cut on the bottom ends of the limb wires and the model bolted to its base. The work of building up the main body bulk can now begin. A series of nails placed every inch along the top and bottom of the centre-board will help in the securing of the main body mass. Fairly coarse wood-wool is used to form most of the body and neck, which is finally covered with fine-grade wood-wool. The nails will enable one to build up the body on one side at a time by simply looping string from a top nail over the wood-wool

body to a bottom nail, moving across from the base of the neck to the pelvis. When both sides have been completed, a much finer wood-wool can be applied, making a neat finish. The finer wood-wool can also be used to form the muscles of the limbs, being bound on to the bones and wire with strong twine.

The specimen is now taking form. Before applying the modelling compound, the bulk of the skull can be made up with fine wood-wool. The cheeks and throat can be secured in place by using strong twine. It is always a good idea to try the skin on to this rough body before continuing. This first fitting gives one a good insight into how much modelling compound is required. To complete the manikin, the muscles are sculptured and the animal form completed in a good modelling compound (papier-mâché). When the body is completely dry the outer surface is sealed (knotting), ready to receive the actual skin. The method described is basically the same as that devised by Karl Akeley, who worked at the Field Museum in Chicago and was well-known for his accurately modelled and hollow body forms. On to the wood-wool form, Akeley applied clay and sculptured the perfect animal. A median line was scratched into the clay from the head to the tail, both above and below the model. The fronts and backs of each leg were also marked and a wall of tin put into place, so that when the body was cast in plaster the complete half would come away and so too would the inside of the front and rear legs. The other side of the body could then be cast in exactly the same way, forming two hollow negative halves of the animal. Papier-mâché was laid into these to make positives, which were then removed from the moulds and trimmed and glued together, making a hollow animal form.

In the early stages the hollow paper forms were known to warp and twist during drying. Therefore, to correct this, Akeley reinforced the form. The inside of the mould was painted with hot animal glue (bead glue). Wet cheese cloth was then stippled into the glue and a coat of papier-mâché spread evenly over it. Akeley then used soft wire cloth No. 24, and eighth-of-an-inch mesh. The mesh, which was galvanised, was laid in the mould and the edges fastened all round by small tacks, which were driven into a square of rubber packing that was set in the plaster mould.

When the mesh had been pushed into place, papier-mâché was applied and forced through the wire, binding it firmly to the first coat. When thoroughly dry, a coat of shellac was given.

To remove the positive from the moulds, they were immersed in water, which seeped into the plaster and soaked up the glue which had previously been painted on to the inside of the mould. The papier-mâché form was then released and lifted out.

Short securing wires were fastened into the lower legs and held in place by more papier-mâché. After trimming, the two halves were held together with wires and glue. The completed form was bolted to its base and the skull fastened to the neck and modelled. The whole animal form was shellacked and allowed to dry before the skin was fitted.

Instead of modelling the animal form with clay, I propose to model the body with modelling compound, so giving a second method in the mounting of larger mammals. Thin modelling compound is applied liberally to the previously dampened wood-wool body. When this is dry the muscle detail is modelled with compound of a thicker consistency. Muscle detail can be given to the four limbs as far down as the toes. After modelling is completed, the skin should have its second fitting, notes being made about the lumps and hollows that occur. When satisfied with the model, give it two good coats of shellac and leave it to dry thoroughly.

Before the skin is finally fitted, cut a large circular hole in either side of the animal body and remove the wood-wool, leaving the form partially hollow and so reducing the weight.

The panels can be replaced and sealed into position with more modelling compound. The body of the specimen is now ready to receive the skin for its final fitting. For the larger mammals it is best to have the skin properly dressed at the tanners (unless one has tanning facilities). One must, of course, tell the tanner that the skin is required for mounting, otherwise the skin would be damaged especially round the face, rendering the whole skin useless for that purpose. To relax the tanned skin, soak it in warm soapy water. When it is relaxed, remove and rinse thoroughly, roll up and store overnight. Next morning it will be found supple and ready for modelling. A good mixture of modelling compound should be made. Some should be the consistency of good workable putty, which will be pushed between the lining of the ears. The remainder should be of a creamy consistency. A generous amount of compound put into the ears can later be forced out to form the strong base of the ears. The thin creamy mixture of modelling compound allows the skin to be slipped about and into the required place. Work from the head end of the specimen,

Plate 1. Wood mouse (*Apodemus sylvaticus*). This small mammal was prepared by freeze-drying (see Chapter 17). The entire specimen is intact, including all internal organs. Only the eyes have been replaced with glass ones.

Plate 2. Steller's eider (*Polysticta stelleri*). This is
probably Europe's rarest breeding duck; it seldom
ventures south of the Arctic circle. This pair was
reared from eggs brought back from Alaska.

Plate 3. Proboscis monkey (*Nasalis larvatus*). This
monkey is found only in Borneo and is a strict
vegetarian, feeding on the leaves, shoots and fruits of
mangroves. This specimen was prepared for display at
Leicester Museum.

Plate 4. (*previous page*). Red deer (*Cervus elephus*). An adult stag will have as many as eight or ten points or tines on each antler (see Chapter 4). These specimens were prepared for museum display.

Plate 5. Primrose (*Primula vulgaris*). This plant was prepared and modelled entirely in wax (see Chapter 19), a most difficult task. Kept in ideal conditions the model will last indefinitely.

Plate 6. Tawny owl (*Strix aluco*). The tawny or brown owl is Britain's most common owl. It is as much at home on the outskirts of large towns as in woodland, and feeds mainly on small mammals, especially voles and mice. Here it is shown pouncing on a wood mouse.

Plate 7. *Top*: Pike (*Esox lucius*). The pike attains lengths of 3½-5 ft and can weigh 60 lb, although specimens of 16-28 lb are usually encountered. *Bottom*: Grayling (*Thymallus thymallus*). A non-migratory salmonid fish, the grayling is particularly appreciated by anglers for its strong fighting spirit. These specimens were prepared by the method described in Chapter 15.

Plate 8. Badger (*Meles meles*). The badger is one of the most elusive of mammals. Nocturnal and generally very wary, it is rarely seen. Scratching posts like the one shown here are found along well-trodden badger paths.

leaving the modelling of the face until later. The skin can be pinned into position as you work, and with the use of strong gut the incision from the throat to the junction of the front legs can be sewn. If the previous fittings of the skin to the manikin have been checked properly, the final positioning of the skin will run smoothly. The edges of the skin should meet evenly, allowing the gut or waxed twine to pull them together. The thin creamy compound will act as a glue, sticking the skin to the model, and creases and wrinkles can be put in the required areas by pushing the skin up from the fur side and holding these in position with galvanised pins knocked into the manikin.

Small galvanised pins are knocked in at intervals along the line of the spine, and also around the root of the tail. These will secure the skin in its natural position. Special care must be taken when dealing with the skin which is hidden under the front legs at their upper junction with the shoulders. These can be tacked after the skin has been sewn together. The same areas of the hind legs are dealt with in a similar manner.

With the belly incision sewn firmly together from lower jaw to vent, one can turn to the inside of each leg. Larger mammals have their hooves removed from the skin. These are cleaned and preserved and fitted in their natural place on the manikin. When fitting the skin of the legs, remember to tuck the skin of the under arm and groin well up between the body and leg. The stitches should be very close, pulling the two parts of the skin firmly together. After completing the stitches, tie off. The skin of the foot should be secured firmly around the crown of the hoof with small galvanised tacks. Attention should now be turned to the vent and tail. Sew the tail along the incision and tie off the twine. The vent should be tucked in and modelled. Small tacks are used to hold it in position.

Modelling the head

The head has been modelled already, but the skin has to be fitted and the animal's outward appearance modelled. First, the ears, previously filled with modelling compound, should be erected in position and the compound squeezed out to form the ear root. Secondly, sharpened wires can be put down the whole length of the ear and forced into the head. It may also be necessary to put some tacks at the root of the ear to hold the skin in the natural contours.

When dealing with large heads, it is always best to fit the eyes before fitting the skin. The skin which has been split around the inside of the eyelids should now have modelling compound put into it and the edges folded inside. The eyelids are now positioned around the glass eye and locked into place. Fit and tack the skin of the lower jaw and mouth to the head form. Modelling compound should be forced into the inside of the nose skin and between the mucous lining and the lips. The skin of the muzzle is now pulled down and modelled in place. Hold the lips and front of the nose in place with long sharp galvanised pins or tacks.

CONTACT CASTING IN FIBRE-GLASS

I first saw the method about to be described in Canada. In essence, the skinned carcass of, for example, a deer or a horse is held in a natural position by some sort of scaffolding and the whole of the carcass covered with a thin layer of fibre-glass. By removing the carcass one is left with a hollow replica of the animal, which is then reinforced, modelled and made to stand up. The skin or hide is fitted and the mount placed into its diorama. But it is not as simple as it sounds. Remember that you are casting dead muscle, which must be remodelled externally later.

I have tried this method and find it very satisfactory. It is in fact a shortened version of the Karl Akeley method, which is described in *Taxidermy and Museum Exhibition* by John Rowley.

Materials

The materials required – polyester resins and glass cloth – are the same as those used in the manufacture of fibre-glass boats, and are readily obtainable, with full instructions for their preparation and temperature requirements. To facilitate removal of the fibre-glass cast from the carcass, a parting agent is first painted on the carcass. 'Partall' is a commercial parting agent used with fibre-glass.

With new fibre-glass materials now available, the animal can be prepared in a fraction of the time required by the earlier method. Taking advantage of technical developments in polyester resins and glass cloth, the preparations such as 'Vultex' and other rubbers, it is now possible to capture the animals in their natural positions and attitudes.

Skinning procedure is the same as in mounting the animal by standard methods. As soon as the skin has been salted and rolled up or sent to the tanners, all internal organs are removed from the body cavity. The cavity is then packed with wood-wool, but before the intestinal cavity is filled and sewn up wire staples should be inserted up through the back to enable the animal to be hung like a puppet from an overhead framework. It can then be manipulated into the position desired. Two hooks, one in each shoulder blade, and two more down the backbone, have been found to be sufficent to support the weight of most animals.

Positioning the carcass

A framework or scaffolding of wood or metal is built in order to suspend the animal carcass while it is being positioned for the application of the fibre-glass. In preparing small mammals, a heavy metal mesh over the top of the framework is convenient, as the strings can be tied anywhere to ensure a good pose.

The positioning of the legs is of great importance. It will be found that hind legs take a natural position and will fall into place, but more care must be taken with the front legs, as the shoulder blades will droop when the mammal is hung. By placing a hook through each shoulder blade one can raise the front leg to its proper position. The legs may have to be held in position by a few wires and have the toes

fastened down.

Care must be taken, when arranging the animal carcass, to visualise the difference the hide, and especially the length of the legs, will make to the finished specimen.

Applying fibre-glass cloth

After the animal's carcass has been arranged in the required attitude, a coat of releasing agent is painted on and allowed to dry. It has been found convenient to cut and fit the fibre-glass cloth to the carcass, holding it in place where necessary with thread and pins. The pieces of glass cloth are overlapped, and tailored to the shape of the animal, to make handling easier.

Two grades of glass cloth, 045 and 031, are used. When covering large animals such as deer, two layers of glass cloth of 031 gauge are used. Two coats of 045 thickness are used on the bodies of smaller mammals, and one coat on the legs. The legs may be reinforced on the inside as described later.

Give the glass cloth a coat of polyester resin, applying it with a paintbrush, being careful not to disturb the arrangement of the cloth which has been placed on the animal. This does become easier with practice. In the case of smaller mammals, for example muntjac or fox, a material such as gauze bandage may be found more suitable for covering the legs. This cloth should be given one or two coats of resin to fill the weave flush with the surface.

Removing the hardened fibre-glass

When the fibre-glass has hardened sufficiently, the opening cuts are made. The size of the mammal and the position in which it is set will determine where the cuts are made. They are normally made along the line between the lower jaw and the vent and on the inside of each leg, but they can be made elsewhere for easier removal of the carcass.

After the carcass has been removed the various pieces will fit together and return to their natural shape. No difficulty will be experienced in matching the opening cuts. They are then sealed together with narrow strips of fibre-glass cloth and resin. Where possible, masking tape is used to hold the seams together while placing narrow strips of cloth on the inside of the legs and the body.

If the animal has very small legs, resin and a material such as powdered slate may be mixed together to the consistency of cream and poured into the legs. The manikin can then be manipulated to allow the creamy mixture to run down the seam, thus sealing it when it is cured.

Leg wires can be fastened in the bottom of the legs by using this same mixture or a commercial body filler intended for filling dents in car bodies.

At this stage the manikin should be nearly ready to receive the skin, depending on how skilfully the animal carcass was arranged at the beginning. Any muscles that have sagged or have not taken proper shape will have to be cut away, the hole patched with fibre-glass and modelled over with papier-mâché, bringing them back to their natural shape. Any other imperfections, such as overlapping edges of the fibre-glass, should be sanded down flush with.the body. Other areas found to be incorrect can be remodelled with papier-mâché. This will bring the manikin to its proper form.

The head of the animal can be done in one of two ways: a cast of the head can be taken, or the original skull can be cleaned, preserved and fitted on to the fibre-glass neck. The cleaned skull is then modelled as already described in previous methods. If you decide to prepare a cast for the head, it can be done as follows.

The head should be put into a freezer. When it is frozen, remove it from the freezer and take a plaster-of-Paris two-piece mould of it by burying half the head in wet sand and building a fence around the exposed half with tin or cardboard.

To prevent the head from sticking to the mould, use a mould release such as olive-oil to grease the head before pouring plaster over the exposed half. As soon as the plaster has hardened, it and the head are removed from the sand and turned over. The other side of the head and the exposed plaster surface are oiled and the fence is placed in position again, so that plaster may be poured over that side.

After the plaster has hardened, the mould is opened by tapping a screwdriver in along the diving line between the two halves. The now thawed animal's head is removed, leaving its exact shape in the plaster.

The two negative halves of the mould are now prepared to receive the fibre-glass which, in turn, will form the two positive halves. When complete, the two halves are fitted together and the head fitted in its rightful place, completing the manikin. The skin of the animal is fitted to the fibre-glass form by glueing, pinning and stitching it into place. The ears are done as described on p. 94 and the face is modelled.

MOUNTING TROPHY HEADS

The smallest heads that are usually mounted as trophies are those of the fox, badger and otter. Hunters may have a wide range of larger heads preserved and set on shields, such as antelope, deer, moose, lion, tiger, hippopotamus and even elephant. All are to be seen hanging in trophy rooms or museums.

When attempting to mount a head, there are various points to be considered. The pelt must be in good condition and, most important, the neck skin must be long enough to give a natural attitude to the head. The skin should be cut back to the shoulders and brisket. A common mistake is to cut the skin of the lower neck too short so that, when the head is mounted, the skin of the lower neck will not reach the back-board. Take heed, therefore, and make sure that plenty of skin is left on the lower neck. Some specimens are best mounted showing the shoulder points and in such cases the skin should be cut right back to include these points.

To skin the heads of horned or antlered animals, follow the method described on pp. 21-2. Heads which carry neither horns nor antlers can be skinned as normal by rolling the skin from neck to nose. The skulls should always be retained, cleaned of all flesh, eyes and brain and placed in a strong salt solution until required. Before mounting, the skull should be boiled, cleaned and dried. There are various ways of reproducing the animal head. First, there is the direct modelling method, which will be explained later. Secondly, there is the contact casting method, where the skinned head and neck are erected in the required position and a thin coat of fibre-glass applied. When the fibre-glass has hardened, it is cut down the face, back of the neck, under the jaw and down the under neck, since this will make it easy to remove the two halves. The two halves of the head and neck are now reinforced on their insides, giving them extra strength, and fitted together. A cut must be made between the lips of the model so that the skin of the lips can be tucked in its natural position.

The head form is fitted to a neck-board which has previously been cut to the correct shape. The completed form is now fitted to a temporary base-board at a comfortable working height. It may be necessary to do some modelling externally before the skin is fitted. Ready-made head forms are obtainable from Jonas Brothers, U.S.A.

The third method is to make a cast of the head and neck. Position them, and make a plaster mould of one side. The dry mould is turned over and a releasing agent applied to the plaster, which is then keyed, and a second mould made. After removing the head and neck, the moulds are sealed and a releasing agent applied to their inner surfaces. The head and neck form is now reproduced in either fibre-glass or papier-mâché. This is then prepared exactly like that produced by the contact casting method.

The last two methods are best used if more than one head is to be mounted, but by far the most skilful method is the direct modelling method.

After removing the skin, lay the head and neck on a piece of board which is about three-quarters of an inch thick. Position as required and with a pencil draw around it, keeping to the natural contours. Before removing the head and neck from the board, make a mark indicating the base of the skull. The whole pencil shape can now be cut out of the board, cutting on the inside of the pencil line. The skull is cut from the neck and is thoroughly cleaned

by immersing it in water, bringing it to the boil and simmering gently until the eyes, brain and all flesh can easily be removed. Cut a board which is the correct shape of the base of the neck and attach it to the neck-board itself. This is then attached to a temporary working base-board. The clean, dry and preserved skull can be fitted to the neck-board by cutting out enough wood to allow the skull to sit in its natural position. The skull is now fixed in place by means of screws and wire.

If the animal's head has to be mounted with its head and neck turned either to the right or the left, substitute two strong wires, by which to support the skull, for the rigid neck-board. As the finished head is to hang on a wall, the size and backward lean of the horns or antlers should also be taken into consideration – the rear-facing tines must clear the wall. The skull and neck-board are now screwed firmly to the temporary working base-board so that modelling can begin. A series of small nails are knocked into the upper and lower edges of the neck-board and around the base-board. They should be inserted at half-inch intervals and left proud. Their function is to hold the twine which is wound around them, thus holding the wood-wool which forms the bulk of the neck muscles in place. Previously damp-ened wood-wool is best used, as this gives greater flexibility. One side of the neck is made up first. To form the windpipe, roll up a length of wood-wool and fix it in position by means of the twine. A second series of nails is now knocked in the side of the neck just behind the wood-wool windpipe. These nails will secure the cot-tons which hold the windpipe, and will give the lower neck its natural shape. Re-peat this process on the other side of the head. When satisfied with the overall shap-ing of the head and neck, the nails can be knocked in and the binding twine secured.

To aid modelling of the muscles, it is advisable to paint on to the wood-wool a thin solution of water, wood-pulp or mashed paper and a little plaster. This will soon harden and form a rigid base on which to model the muscle detail. Mix sufficient modelling compound to com-plete the job. I find the best medium for

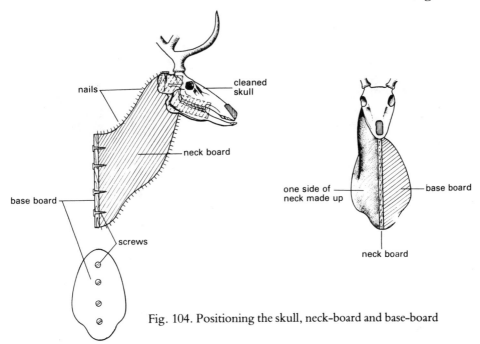

Fig. 104. Positioning the skull, neck-board and base-board

this job is papier-mâché mixed with water, animal glue, whiting, plaster and fine sawdust. Mix to a consistency which allows easy modelling.

Cover the whole head and neck with the compound and smooth it all over with the aid of a small trowel. Now, model the cheeks, nose and lips. Before the modelling compound dries completely, scrape out the groove of the mouth between the lips, which will ultimately secure the lip skin in position. When the whole of the trophy head is thoroughly dry it can be smoothed to perfection with sandpaper.

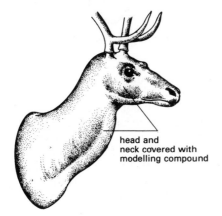

Fig. 105. Modelling the head and neck

Paint the whole form with a sealer and waterproof it with two coats of shellac. It is now ready to receive the skin.

Mounting and modelling the head

The trophy skin can be pickled in a brine solution as already described for larger mammal skins, or it can be sent to the tanners to be dressed. Before the skin is treated with pickle or sent to the tanners, the mucous lining of the lips must be split and roughly pared down. The skin around the eyes should be dealt with in a similar manner. The skin of the ears should be split from the cartilage or, as some preparators prefer, the complete ear cartilage should be removed. The cartilage is later replaced with either thin tin or stiff card. If the cartilage is left in the ear then it is reinforced by squeezing in modelling compound.

Lastly, the cartilage must be removed from the nose. Leave the internal skin of the nostrils as long as possible, so that they can be well tucked into the model nose of the head form. When the skin has been preserved, mounting can begin.

Fill the ears with modelling compound and put a little around the eye skin. A thick

93

Taxidermy

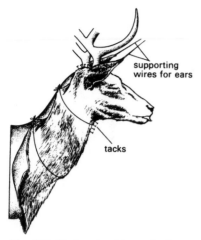

Fig. 106. Fitting the skin to the form

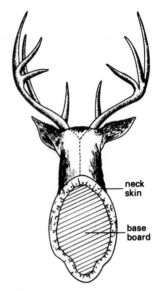

Fig. 107. Tacking the neck-skin to the base-board

sticky solution of the modelling compound is made up, omitting the sawdust
and papier-mâché, or casein glue thick-
ened with flour paste. This is painted on to
the form and the head skin fitted.

To ensure that the skin is sitting correctly, a series of headless galvanised tacks
are knocked into the neck-board along the
lower neck. Stitch the incision along the
back of the neck with strong waxed twine.
A series of galvanised tacks can also be
knocked in along this line. The skin will
now stick and fit to the contours of the
form. Tacks can be knocked into various
places to hold it secure. Tuck the lip skin
into the groove provided, and hold it in
place with tacks. Place some modelling
compound around the nose and tuck the
nose skin well into the model and secure.
The eyes can be fitted at this stage (or they
could have been set into the orbits provided
on the model before the skin was fitted).

Special care should be exercised here as
the eyes are the focal point of the whole
job. Hold the skin around the eyes in place
with plenty of securing tacks.

Lastly, the ears are modelled by squeezing the compound from their tips and into
the base. A strong supporting wire is put
down the whole length of the ear and
knocked firmly into the head. Allow the
modelling compound to become hard by
leaving it overnight. Then remove the
mounted head from its temporary base in
order to secure the skin at the base of the

Fig. 108. The finished head

neck. Pull it firmly around the neck base-
board and tack it into position. Replace the
trophy and leave it until thoroughly dry.

If the head form has been modelled exactly, it is merely a case of fitting and tacking
the skin in place. The fitting of the eyes is by
far the most difficult part of the whole job.
They are so important because they are the
key to a natural or unnatural head.

OPEN-MOUTH MODELLING

At some stage you will have to model the internal structure of the open mouth of a specimen. It may be the open mouth of a crocodile, snake, bird or a mammal. The same ingredients are used in each case to reproduce the soft fleshy internal structure.

If the specimen is fresh, moulds are made of the various parts of the mouth. For instance, the roof of the mouth and the tongue can be moulded with a cold cure rubber. These two parts can now be reproduced in fibre-glass, the resin having been previously tinted to the required colour. Before casting the tongue, make sure that it occupies the correct position relevant to the attitude of the specimen. For a snarling lion or tiger, it will be drawn out of the way of the canines and sucked towards the throat, so that it has a high hump in the centre. Then detach the tongue from the mouth of the specimen.

The tongue must be prepared before casting. It should be washed in borax water to remove all mucus and placed in a solution of one-third alcohol and two-thirds water until required. After removing it from the alcohol, lay it on a bed of clay. Build a retaining wall around it, pour on the rubber solution, and when dry remove it. The rubber mould can be painted with the coloured fibre-glass gel coat and reinforced with strand matting. If the original tongue and roof of the mouth are not available then these are best modelled in clay and moulded as already described.

Mix a good quality modelling compound/papier mâché and pre-colour it to correspond with the gullet and gums. Place a liberal amount on the back of the mouth and gullet and beneath the place where the tongue will be. With tiny brass screws, screw the fibre-glass roof of the mouth in place after embedding it in compound. The screws can be covered with the same coloured resin later. Push the tongue into the modelling compound and with a wet paint brush model this area, smoothing and forming it around the tongue. Put modelling compound around the teeth of both upper and lower jaws to form the gums and again smooth and model them around the roots of the teeth. When the modelling of the mouth is complete and dry, the mouth must appear moist. This is achieved by painting the whole of the mouth with a clear gloss paint or a mixture of 2 oz white beeswax, 2 oz paraffin wax and 1 oz rosin. Melt the ingredients in a double boiler as described for animal glue. Pre-colour as required, and paint the molten wax on to the tongue, the inside of the mouth and the gums.

The modelling of the mouth in mammals should be done before fitting the head skin. The lips of the head skin must be split, so that a large amount of skin is left on the inside of the lip, which can be tucked in when the lips are being modelled. They should also be pared down well, with little room left for shrinkage. Fit and glue the head skin on to the head form, and place the well-mixed modelling compound in the split lips, tucking the inside skin over the compound, sandwiching it to form the fulness of the lip itself. The skin glue can now be painted on the undersides of the lips all around the mouth and the mouth modelled to the desired attitude. Long, strong, sharp galvanised pins are made from various wires and knocked into the lips and round the mouth, holding them until the compound becomes rock hard.

A final touching up is needed before applying any clear varnish or coloured wax and so completing the structure of the mouth. The modelling of mouths is an extremely skilled job and perfect success comes only from years of experience.

Dental suppliers are the obvious people to approach for advice on the reproduction of tongues and gums. A product called Simplex Rapid, an acrilic dental repair material, will be found most useful for the hand modelling of tongues. It is a pink powder which is mixed with a liquid hardener. One must experiment in order to achieve perfection when preparing tongues in this way. Mix the powder and liquid together and when the mixture becomes fairly stiff pick it up and knead it. When it starts to harden it will do so quickly, so place the still soft hand-modelled tongue into the lower jaw, fitting and modelling until it becomes stiffer. The final texture of the tongue, i.e. the central groove and various ridges, are modelled just before the compound sets hard. A much thinner mixture of this material is ideal for the modelling of the gums – the translucent effect given by Simplex Rapid produces a very real and lifelike copy.

14

Skinning and Mounting Fish

When beginning the preparatory work in the setting up of fish, it is important to choose a species whose scales are firmly attached. Fish such as carp or bream (*Cyprinidae*) have large loose-fitting scales which are easily dislodged.

The best species to choose are either pike (*Esocidae*) or bass (*Serranidae*). Many anglers prefer to have the skin of the actual specimen they fought so hard to land preserved and mounted, rather than having a cast made. But casting techniques have reached such a high standard that they are far superior to the preparation of fish by the traditional skinning method.

The best side of the fish should be chosen and a photograph taken for future reference. The specimen should have alum, borax or table salt sprinkled over its surface to remove the slime from the body. The skin should next be lightly oiled (best with olive-oil) which will act as a releasing agent when a cast of the fish is made.

To make a negative mould of the fish, prepare a box of the correct size, and half fill it with sand. Cover the sand with an oil cloth or greaseproof paper, to prevent the sand adhering to the fish. Make a depression in the sand which will allow the fish to

sink into it, so preventing any undercuts when the mould is made.

Dental plaster should be mixed with water with the hands to squeeze out any lumps, until it reaches a creamy consistency. Pour the plaster over the specimen and tap the sides of the casting box to ensure that the plaster reaches all areas. When the plaster is completely dry, remove it from the box and extract the fish. The mould can now be placed on one side until required.

Wipe the show side of the fish with a damp cloth, removing any powder or remnants of plaster. Lightly oil it again. Place tissue paper on top of the oiled surface and pat down firmly. The paper will help to hold the scales in position while the body is removed from the skin. Turn the fish over on to the show side in preparation for making an incision. Lightly oil or glycerine the fins to prevent them from drying out during skinning.

SKINNING THE FISH

The initial incision is made along the whole length of the lateral line, from

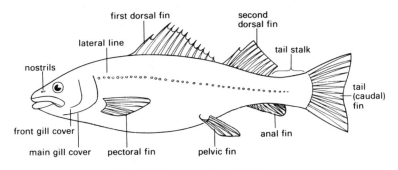

Fig. 109. Topography of a fish

97

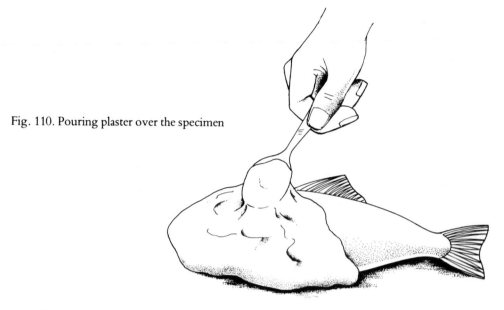

Fig. 110. Pouring plaster over the specimen

shoulder to tail fin.

Use fairly heavy scissors or tinner's shears for this job. At the end of the tail make a further cut, following the natural curve of the tail. With a scalpel or dull knife, cut the skin free from the flesh on both sides. When you reach the dorsal fin, and the pectoral and ventral fins, cut through their bony structures with heavy scissors or shears, freeing them from the body mass. The skin can now be freed from the flesh until it lies flat on the table surface.

Remember to leave the skin flat on the table surface without too much disturbance. The body should be lifted from the skin; sideways manipulation of the fish skin does no harm, but any endwise rolling can cause the epidermis to break, releasing scales from their seats.

Fig. 111. First incision

Fig. 112. Freeing the skin from the flesh

In order to lift the body skin, the vertebrae must be severed as close to the tail fin as possible. Care must be taken not to cut the skin in any way. Place the palm of the hand on the tail fin and with the other hand take hold of the tail just behind the cut. Now work the fingers and thumb round the tail and pull gently, easing the body from the skin just enough to allow the dull knife to be used to release the body. Once a start has been made, the body can be lifted and the knife used to free it from the skin. Do not worry about leaving large chunks of flesh on the skin. These can be removed when the main body bulk is out of the way.

When the skin is free as far as the shoulder girdle, the body can be laid back down in its natural position. With heavy scissors or shears, cut through the shoulder girdle and the body vertebrae, as near to the skull as possible. When this is done, a little further manipulation will be necessary to remove the body mass.

Dealing with the head is the most tedious part of the whole operation, since it is the part most likely to decompose if not properly handled. Special care must be exercised with the throat. This is attached below the lower jaw and appears as a single membrane. The membrane opens up and joins the body skin at the junction with the pectoral fins. The skin of the throat can be split and its fleshy interior removed from each side of the flimsy bone which lies within. I find it much easier to clean the inside of the head by removing the gills first. These are easily cut at their upper and lower ends and taken out. With a curved instrument, remove the eyeballs. Now cut around the inside of their rims, to open a way for extracting the cheek muscles. After opening the gill covers wide, sharp scissors can be inserted and the inner bony structure, which holds the cheek muscles in place, can be cut away and discarded. The inside of the lower jaw often has much flesh attached. This must be removed and the lower jaw scraped clean. Fish such as pike have a large number of very sharp teeth, so that the task of removing flesh from the jaws is hazardous and painful. Finally, cut a hole in the cranium and take out the brain. A general clean up of all the flesh still adhering to the inside of the head should now be undertaken.

Spread the body skin flat, and with a scraper remove all the fat and flesh. An ideal scraper can be made by cutting the tip off a spoon and making serrations in its flat end. If you bend the head of the spoon at right angles, it will be ready to be used as an efficient instrument. When scraping, remember to scrape from tail to head, and not *vice versa,* for if you scrape in the opposite direction the scales are likely to be popped out of their seats.

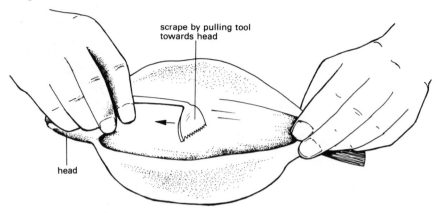

Fig. 113. Scraping the fat and flesh from the skin

When you have cleaned the skin, place the whole specimen in a bath of water and wash it thoroughly. Drain and preserve it with borax and tannic acid mix, or the non–poisonous soap-based preservative of Montagu Browne (see p. 27). It can now be stored in a polythene bag or box while the mould is prepared.

MOUNTING THE SKIN

Submerge the plaster mould in water for about half an hour. This will aid in the extraction of the sand or sawdust-filled body later. Shake off any excess water and lay the skin into the mould, making sure that the skin fits exactly.

Lift the gill cover and fill the show-side cheek, which is lying at the bottom of the plaster mould. This is best filled out with good quality papier-mâché. Next fill the upper cheek. The strip of skin which forms the throat should now be filled with papier-mâché and the two edges loosely sewn together. These strips of skin will be covered when both gills are together in their natural position.

The mouth and the rest of the interior of the head should now be filled to capacity, using a light papier-mâché. This should finish around the base of the skull. Make two holes with a leather punch, one on either side of the severed horny arch on which the gill covers lie. These are now tied together, and the skin can be sewn up, beginning at the gill end. Sew about three inches. Then sew the skin of the tail, after embedding the roots in papier-mâché. Again sew for a distance of three inches.

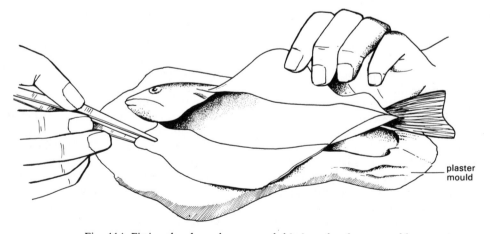

Fig. 114. Fitting the cleaned, preserved skin into the plaster mould

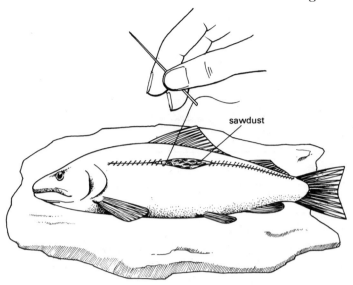

sawdust

Fig. 115. Sewing up the incision

Damp sawdust or sand is now employed to fill the body of the fish. It must be packed in very tightly. Any area not filled will cause a depression in the finished specimen. Sew the skin together as you proceed, first from the head end and then from the tail. Having packed the sawdust or sand in tightly, you will arrive at the centre of the body. Fill the skin to capacity and tie the two sewing ends together completing the filling.

The specimen must now be removed from the mould. If there are any under-cuts, the removal of the fish will be hampered and the mould may have to be broken. Having removed the specimen successfully, turn it over (show-side up) and place it on to a wire drying-tray or something similar. Air must be able to circulate freely around the body. Ensure that the mouth is closed and remove papier-mâché from the eye-socket to make room for the eye, which is fitted when the skin is dry. Wipe the fish with a damp cloth to remove dust and plaster.

A diluted solution of formaldehyde of 5 per cent is brushed on to the skin to fix it into position. The fins are treated in a similar way, but first they are carded.

Carding the fins

The fins must be spread as in life and placed between two pieces of stiff cardboard. For larger fish, thin plywood can be substituted. The card is held together with paper clips which may have to be opened slightly, and pins. Fins like the pectorals are held off the body in their natural swimming position, by propping them up with cotton-wool or blocks of balsa wood.

Lay the specimen on one side, and allow it to dry. When it is thoroughly dry insert the eye, embedding it in modelling compound or papier-mâché. Clear flat eyes, painted exactly like the original, are the best to use.

The mounted specimen, now dry and firm, should have the filling removed. First cut a fairly large oblong hole each side of the incision in the centre of the body. Holding the tail and allowing the head to hang down over a receptacle ease out the filling by means of a flat piece of wood with a rounded end. When the filling is out of the tail end, a final tap or two will dislodge the remaining sawdust or sand. Holding the specimen by the head, proceed in the same way until all the filling is removed. It is always a good idea to blow out any remaining grains with compressed air. The empty cavity can now be shellacked and loosely filled with fine wood-wool, or reinforced with fibre-glass.

In order to fit the fish on to a backboard or into a case, cut two wooden cleats. These

101

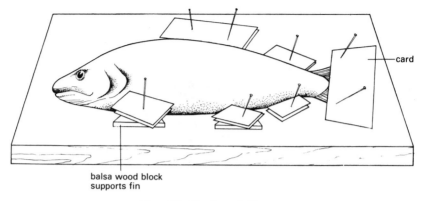

card

balsa wood block
supports fin

Fig. 116. Carding the fins

should be about a third of the length of the fish body. You may have to open the incision a little to allow the inside cleat to be fitted. When the inside cleat is secure, the outer one can be screwed in place, so sandwiching the skin. Another way is to prepare a thicker piece of wood, which is attached to the inside of the skin by embedding it in modelling compound or fibre-glass. Tack the back skin to it. The specimen can be attached to its backboard or case by screwing through the backboard or case.

PAINTING THE FISH

Before painting the specimen – which, incidentally, is the most difficult part of the process of mounting fish – the fins may need to be repaired and reinforced. Tissue paper or very fine muslin is used and stuck to the underside of the fin. An instant glue or one of the resins can be used for this. Any large gaps in the fins can be filled in very successfully with the celluloid recipe given in Chapter 6.

After repairing the fins, the whole specimen should be made waterproof by coating with clear varnish or shellac. It is now ready to be painted properly. Everyone has his own technique in the painting of fish, so there are no hard and fast rules. First, the ground colour must be applied – usually very pale belly, becoming darker towards the back and finally very dark on the back and head. Then, once the ground colour is dry, the specimen should be placed against a light background and the

35 mm transparency projected on to it. Make sure that the slide projection is exact. This is a great asset and does help one to distinguish the variation in colours and markings. But this is not the whole answer. It is simply an aid to check and recheck the colours. Winsor and Newton or similar oil colour is used, with refined linseed oil and turpentine to make the colour easier to apply. The large areas of ground colour are best applied by spraying, blending one tone into another. The finer parts, such as spots and lines, can only be put on with a good quality brush.

Crec-o-pearl essence

Pearl essence was first discovered by a French rosary maker named Jacquin in the seventeenth century. He used to coat beads to resemble natural pearls, and this use has continued ever since. It was not until more recent years that pearl essence was used to decorate leather, paper, metal, wood, plastics and such items as wax flowers, candles and plaster cake decorations. Its more recent use is as an addition to nail varnish, lipstick and other cosmetic items.

Natural pearl essence is a suspension of guanine crystals in a solvent such as butyl acetate, a plasticiser such as dioctyl phthalate, or a vehicle such as nitrocellulose. While guanine is widely distributed in the animal kingdom, it occurs only occasionally in the particular crystalline form suitable for use as pearl essence.

The scales of fish such as bleak, herring, sardine and brisling are collected and treated to remove the 'fish silver' from the horny scale, which is then discarded. The fish silver is further purified to remove the thin layer of fatty tissue surrounding the guanine crystals, until only uniform crystals of pure guanine remain. The care taken in this process and the degree of purity which is achieved determine the quality of the final product.

The pearl essence must be mixed with a clear dope which will act as a vehicle, making it easier to apply. It is only necessary to touch the edges of each scale to give a really original effect when completed. This, needless to say, is a most laborious task.

15

Casting Fish

Casting fish is by no means a modern method of presentation. Many methods were evolved in which the final product contained little or no part of the original fish, the reproduction being a painted cast in plaster of Paris or a tissue paper or glue lay-up in a mould (in this case backed by modelling clay and wood-wool as a body filler to give strength). Both these methods had the obvious drawbacks of producing heavy or fragile reproductions. But both gave extremely realistic representations of fish as far as shape was concerned, as compared with those produced by the more usual method of skinning and mounting. Here, lack of control during the drying of the skin, shrinkage of the tissues of the head and the need to remodel this part of the fish tended to produce fish which were no longer the smooth streamlined creatures of nature but rather grotesque caricatures of their former selves.

To overcome these problems, a method was devised of mounting the skin while it was kept inside a mould, taken from the fish before skinning. While the shape of the body may have improved in this way, the head still required remodelling to give it a natural look.

As with casts, painting therefore had to be undertaken when the skin was used because of remodelling of the head. Furthermore, even the body and fins had to be painted because of fading of the colours of the fish since no method of preservation of the skin had or has been devised which will preserve their colours in their natural intensity.

The advent of plastics, in the form of resins, together with glass-cloth, means that casts can now be produced which are not only very strong but also light in weight. A method of producing a realistic cast of a fish in side view is given here.

Once experience has been gained in carrying out a simple cast from a one-piece mould, more complicated casts of fish in action poses can be undertaken.

MAKING THE MOULD

Since the quality of the mould will depend to a great extent on the state of the specimen, great care must be taken in the preparation of the specimen. This preparation can often take longer than making the mould itself.

All frozen specimens must be thoroughly thawed out. Not only is the setting of plaster-of-Paris affected by low temperature, but flexibility of the specimen is reduced by the presence of ice crystals in the tissues, so that the fish cannot be placed in the desired position.

The thawing out of specimens should be done in water, so that there is no dehydration of the fins and skin, which would reduce mobility.

Very light-coloured or whitish areas on the body, especially on the fins of frozen specimens, are indications of frost-burn, a form of dehydration akin to freeze-drying. Such specimens, or badly dehydrated specimens, should be placed in a 5 per cent aqueous solution of tri-sodium ortho-phosphate for a period of time to allow them to rehydrate.

Considerable amounts of water may be taken up by a specimen in this solution after a few days, when it will become relatively firm, even if somewhat smelly. All specimens, whether fresh or frozen, will need to be properly cleaned, as the mucus-producing cells of many species remain active for a considerable time after death. The dehydrated slime of frozen specimens

Fig. 117. Cleaned specimen on a polythene sheet

will increase greatly in volume on thawing out, especially when this is done in water as recommended.

Finely powdered alum carefully sprinkled on to the specimen and gently worked over the surface from tail to head will readily coagulate the mucus and thus allow the slime to be removed. This must be done with great care, especially if the fish in question has scales that are easily detached.

If the specimen is wanted for eating, alum can obviously not be used. But with a little more work the same results can be achieved using cooking salt (sodium chloride).

The specimen should now be washed in running water to remove all alum or salt and then be allowed to dry. (Several applications may be necessary, as some species, such as skates and rays, tend to produce large amounts of mucus, especially if relatively fresh.)

The cleaned specimen is now placed on a polythene covered sheet of soft-board or sandela. The sheet should be large enough to support the specimen and plaster of the mould and should also be strong enough to take the weight of both, as the board will be needed to lift both the specimen and the plaster of the mould when turning them over for moulding on the reverse side.

A specimen placed on its side as above, and cast in this position represents the simplest of casts. Action poses, such as leaping, require a deep-sided casting box in which the specimen can be set out. Even a whole cast, i.e. one in which both sides will be complete in the round, should be bedded on deep sand within a box, rather than on a flat board.

Remove the pectoral and pelvic fins only, by cutting them off at the natural joint lying just under the surface of the body. Each fin should be separately labelled so that they cannot be mixed up. (In the case of *Salmo* species or other types which bear an adipose fin, this too should be cut off, and like the other fins, should be kept in a standard solution of phenol for temporary preservation.) *The fins should be removed with great care so as not to penetrate into the body cavity of the fish.*

Polystyrene blocks are now placed under the dorsal and anal fins so as to keep them in the median plane of the fish's body, and the fins are erected or arranged as desired. The blocks should protrude slightly from the fins at their leading and trailing edges only, and should have sides which slope away from the fins to the baseboard. This will allow not only their subsequent removal from the mould when the reverse side of the fin has to be cast, but

105

also the removal of the mould pieces themselves from the main mould part.

The polystyrene blocks are now pinned to the baseboard so that they will not move, as are the fins to the blocks in their required position. (This should be done with fine entomological pins from which the heads have been removed.)

The tail is similarly pinned to the board with pins fixed through the outermost rays.

At this stage it will have been noticed that the abdominal region of the fish is relatively flabby and often collapsed. The only thing that can be done to regain some of the solid appearance is to fill the abdomen to support its walls and so prevent them from falling inwards. A lot of trouble can be taken in filling the belly with soft clay introduced from the rear side of the body through an incision, and moulding the clay to shape from the show side. This will often prove difficult, as the points of finger pressure used to mould the clay will remain in the tissue as shallow pits. But if air is carefully injected into the abdomen between the intestine and abdominal wall, much of the tightness and shape of the belly can be regained. Care should be taken not to overinject, as this will give the fish a plump appearance and will pull at the fins which are already set out. Injection may be

achieved by means of a very large syringe and fine needle in small fish, or through a needle attached to a compressor hose. In either case, the needle, introduced between the scales from the rear, or at the point of cut-off of the fins, should not be removed until the correct shape has been achieved. (The injection of air may force the intestine to emerge through the anus, or may force some of the gut content to spill out. A plug of cotton-wool will prevent either from happening.)

Injection of water into the abdomen should not be tried, as the weight of the water will cause more distortion than it alleviates. But the eyes, which will undoubtedly also have collapsed, may be injected with water to bring them back to shape, the water being injected into the rear of the eye, which is turned to one side.

The fish can now be surrounded with a wall to prevent the moulding plaster from running too far from the body of the fish. The depth of the retaining wall will depend on the size of the fish or its relative depth. The fish is now ready for casting.

The fish must be inspected again for acceptability of position, since the moment has come after which alterations to the cast can only be made with the greatest difficulty, if at all.

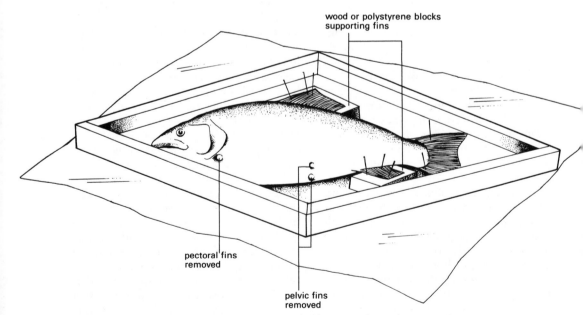

wood or polystyrene blocks supporting fins

pectoral fins removed

pelvic fins removed

Fig. 118. Specimen surrounded by a wood or polystyrene frame

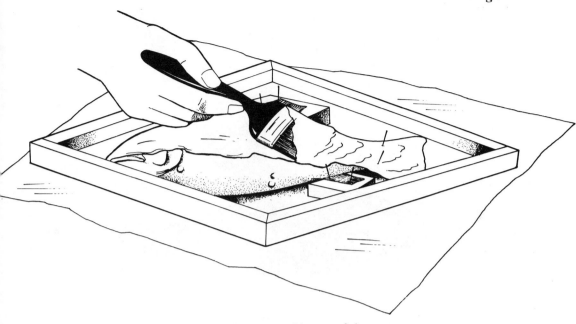

Fig. 119. Painting on a thin coat of plaster

All materials and utensils required in making the mould – a brush, a large cup, several mixing pails and a cut length of coarse hessian bandage, as well as an ample supply of plaster-of-Paris – should be at hand.

A first coat of thin plaster-of-Paris, the consistency of cream, is now applied to the fish with a paintbrush – the plaster being brushed on from the tail to the head.

The plaster is now brushed off gently in the opposite direction – head to tail. (This will make certain that the plaster comes into the closest possible contact with the scales, so that the greatest detail of scaling is picked up.) The rest of the initial plaster mix should be poured from a cup along the midline of the fish, so as to run down each side of the body and over the head, fins and tail. If this is properly carried out, it should be possible to cover the whole fish with just under half an inch of plaster. Considering that this stage of the moulding process must be performed without a break, it is obvious that the plaster must be mixed in such a way that it can be painted on and then poured on. Enough plaster to complete the operation in one go must be mixed, and mixed so that it does not set before this part is completed. If the plaster does begin to set, it

should not be used after it stops being free running, as it will only tend to force off the plaster already on the fish, this plaster taking slightly longer to set than the bulk plaster in the mixing pail.

The initial thickness of plaster of just under half an inch should be increased for large soft specimens, such as sharks, as it will have to support the weight of subsequent layers of plaster without breaking or cracking.

A second coat of plaster is applied once the first has set. This and subsequent coats of plaster, however, should contain reinforcement in the form of coarse hessian. Strips (of half the length of the fish) are held at one end in a spread position and dipped into the plaster. As excess plaster is being brushed from the strip over the edge of the mixing pail, the length of the strip is gradually laid along the length of the fish in such a way that it falls down evenly without the need for folds to be straightened out.

This is repeated until the whole fish has at least one length-wise covering of hessian and plaster, when a cross-wise application is given. The edge of the mould (against the frame) should also be reinforced, as it must not only be able to take the weight of

107

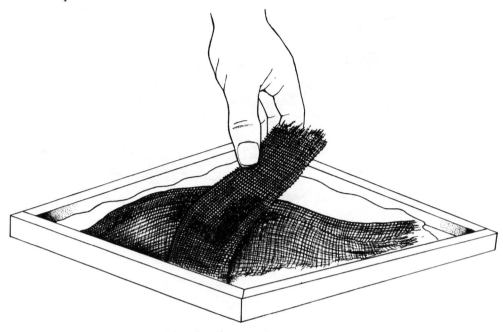

Fig. 120. Applying strips of hessian to reinforce the plaster

the fish and mould when these are turned over, but also be sufficiently thick to allow keys to be carved in it for locating other mould pieces.

Any mixed plaster should be poured over the mould to strengthen it further, especially if the fish is a large one. (If you are in doubt about the strength of the mould, always add more plaster reinforced with hessian, since a cracked or broken mould is very difficult to repair.)

The wall surrounding the cast is removed after the final coat of plaster has been allowed to set for half an hour or so.

The mould with fish is now turned over on to its back, support during the operation being gained from the board on which the fish had originally been placed.

The polystyrene blocks supporting the fins are now removed, as are the pins which held the fins to the blocks. This can only be done, of course, if the heads have been cut off before the show-side was cast.

Any plaster which covers the underside of the fins due to under-running during the casting of the show-side should now be removed to expose the whole of the reverse side of the dorsal and ventral fins.

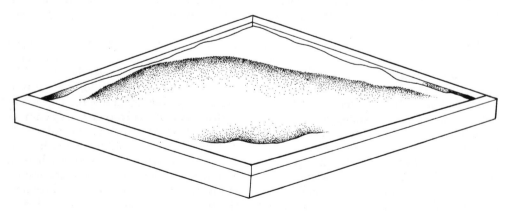

Fig. 121. Final plaster coat

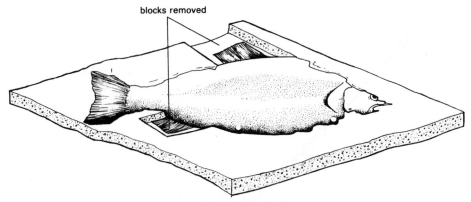

blocks removed

Fig. 122. Blocks supporting the fins are removed

Any rough areas on the plaster around the fins should be made smooth, while all small holes which may act as holding keys between the mould pieces should be filled with modelling clay or plasticene.

Two small keys (conical depressions) either round or elongated, should be cut into the plaster surface surrounding the fin. To prevent the plaster of the new mould pieces from sticking to the main mould, a separator such as soft soap, shellac or one of the modern separators based on polyvinyl alcohol, (e.g. liquid tin foil – a separator used extensively in dentistry), must be applied over the area of the mould likely to come into contact with new plaster.

The depressions, representing the fin-support blocks, are now filled with plaster in much the same way as the main part of the mould was produced.

After the setting of the plaster, the small mould pieces are carefully removed by levering them apart with chisels inserted on the outer seam between them. Plaster may therefore have to be cut away to expose the join. The fish may be moved from the mould once the mould pieces have been separated.

This operation generally requires two people, one to hold the mould at the head end, the other to lift the fish from the mould at the tail. The wrist of the tail, since it is generally rather solid, may cause some difficulty, especially as there is frequently a lot of plaster under-run. A little cutting away of the plaster and slow twisting of the tail should allow this part of the fish to be freed from the mould.

Slide a hand under the body of the fish towards the head to free the body of the fish from the mould as far as the edge of the gill covers. This generally tends to stick in the mould because of the under-run of plaster. But at this stage it should be easy to

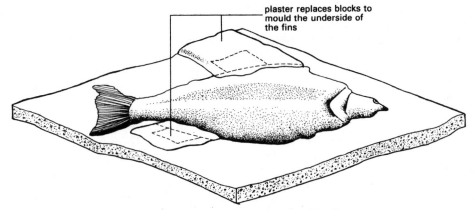

plaster replaces blocks to mould the underside of the fins

Fig. 123. Moulding the underside of the fins

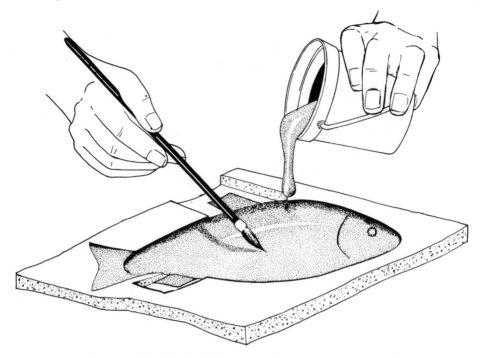

Fig. 124. Applying a coat of gel-coat resin

assess the success of the mould-making operation as far as detail of scaling and definition is concerned. If the first is satisfactory and a second is not needed, or if indeed the fish has suffered considerable scale loss (those sticking to the plaster) so that a second coat is not possible, remove the body and head if necessary by cutting piece by piece from the mould to ensure that the cast remains undamaged. Otherwise brute strength and back tugging (hence the person holding the head) should free the fish from the mould.

Any large pieces which have broken out of the mould should be retained, as they can easily be glued back into position before casting.

The mould pieces should now all be put together and the whole lot be bound up with a one-inch-wide rubber band cut from the inner tube of a pneumatic tyre. The bound-up mould should be dried, preferably in a warm atmosphere (for speed) until the plaster has a dry feel and the mould gives a clear ring when tapped.

MAKING THE CAST

The pieces of the mould are separated from one another once dry, and all surfaces bearing details of the fish, as well as the surface around them, are sealed with at least two coats of thinned shellac. Allow enough time for each coat to dry. The sealed surfaces are then given two coats of separator, which may be a beeswax and turpentine (one pound to two pints) solution or one of the proprietory water-soluble separators based on polyvinyl alcohol (PVA). (This is the best separator available and every effort should be made to obtain it.)

After the separator has been allowed to dry thoroughly, the surface carrying details of the fish is given a generous coat of gel-coat resin carrying white pigment.

The main exception to gel-coating is the fin surfaces. Those of the main mould (show-side) are given only a thin coat, while those of the small mould are allowed to remain without. (These surfaces do not get any resin until they are ready to be joined up.)

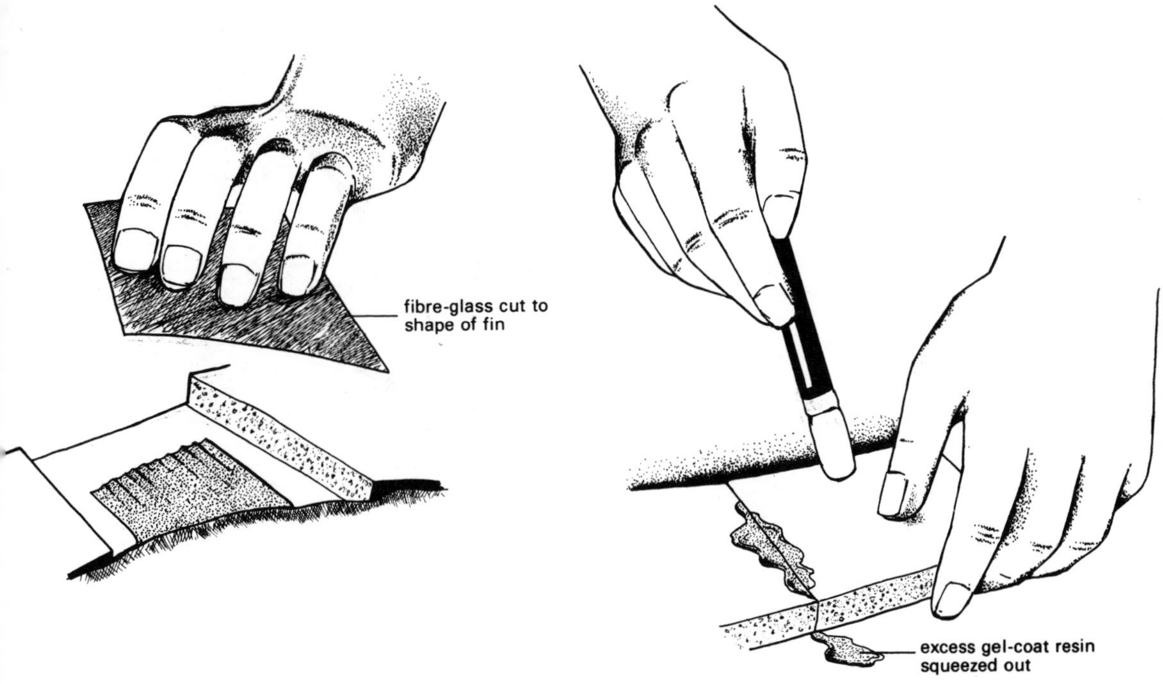

fibre-glass cut to
shape of fin

excess gel-coat resin
squeezed out

Fig. 125. Casting the fins

At least two layers of glass-fibre resin should be applied to the mould, apart from the fin areas.

When the resin has completely set, trial fittings of the mould pieces are made. Undoubtedly they will not fit properly, as even with the greatest care some resin will have got into the flat surface between the mould pieces, or the gel-coat on the show side mould will be too thick. The resin from the mould surfaces must be removed, as must the excess from the fin (with care, of course).

With the pieces fitting properly the fin area of the show side is now given a layer of glass fibre and gel-coat, the glass–cloth having been cut to fit the shape of the fin. Excess gel-resin is now applied to the fin surface of the small mould piece (the reverse side), which is then pressed into position in the main mould. If properly executed, a large amount of excess resin should ooze from between the mould pieces.

A strip of glass–cloth can now be placed over the inner join of the mould pieces.

The complete casting of the fins must be carried out as a single operation without setting of the resin, which may therefore have to be prepared as a slow mix.

A block of wood can also be fixed into the hollow body of the fish with strips of glass and resin, so that a backboard can be screwed to it for painting and ultimate display.

When the resin has set, the whole cast and mould should be soaked for about six to nine hours in warm water before the mould is broken up and the cast is removed from it.

Care should be taken during removal of the cast from the mould. While a hammer may successfully be used to break down the structure of the mould, the use of chisels to remove the plaster should be avoided, as they can easily go too deep and thus damage the cast.

Thin layers of plaster which may adhere to the cast can easily be removed by further soaking with boiling water and vigorous brushing with a hard bristle brush.

The excess resin and glass – the casting 'flash' – from around the cast has to be removed, using either a miniature drill

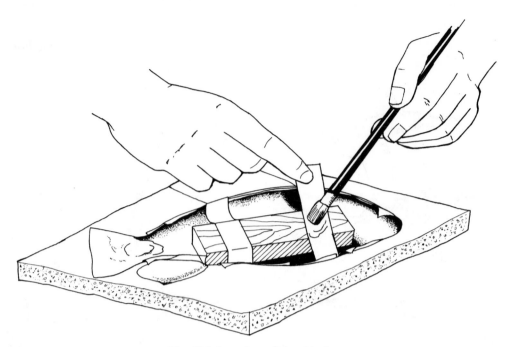

Fig. 126. Inserting a fixing block

Fig. 127. Removing the cast
from the mould.

plaster mould

fibre-glass cast

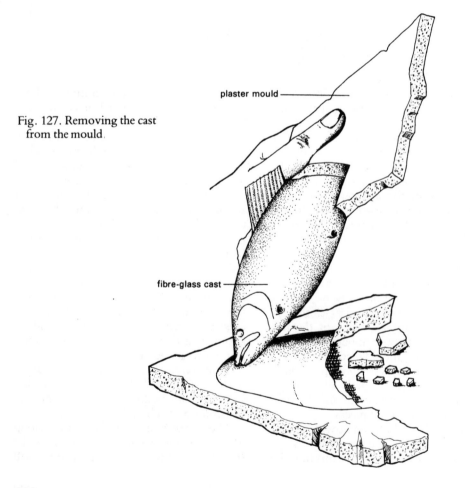

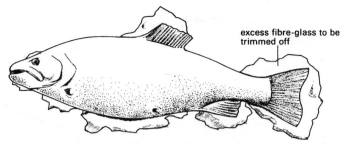

Fig. 128. The cast before trimming

with flexible drive (like a dental drill) or modelling files.

Any defects in the cast must now be made good, with holes being modelled out (using one of the many 'body-fillers' employed in the car body repair trade), and unwanted bumps removed. Some reinforcement of detail not picked up by the mould can now be made.

Only detailed knowledge of fish or comparison of the cast with the actual fish can indicate where individual casts need modelling work. Experience will show that the area around the rear edge of the gill-covers and the maxillary and gap of the mouth require the most modelling work.

The paired fins

The paired fins, i.e. the pelvic and pectoral fins which have been kept in the phenol solution, are now made ready for ultimate addition to the cast. Two choices are open – to use them either in a dried state or as casts. In either case they should be pinned out into the position wanted on the cast. If casts are desired, a mould is made of the fins' two surfaces in such a way that two halves result – halves which can be joined together exactly with respect to each other through adequate keying.

Such moulds should be dried, sealed and given coats of separator like the main cast. Each fin surface in the mould is given an exact thin coat of white gel-resin only.

When this has set, a piece of glass-cloth of exact fin size and shape is laid up on one of the two mould halves. Before this can set, an obvious excess of resin is applied to each surface and the mould is closed, the excess resin being squeezed out. Once the process is complete, as soon as the resin has set but is not yet cured, soaking of the moulds in warm water is advised. The halves can then be separated while the resin is still flexible and not brittle, so that the fins will bend rather than fracture if handled roughly during removal from the mould. As for the main cast, trimming and perhaps some modelling may have to be undertaken. If, on the other hand, it has been decided to use the actual fins – and this can nearly always be done with fins which are not particularly fleshy – they are simply allowed to dry out in their pinned out positions.

After thorough drying, thin wires – about three inches long – are inserted into the base of the fins, so that they can now be stored in a vertical position with the wires as stands.

Since the drying out has reduced the thickness of the fins, they should be coated with one or more layers of thin resin catalysed to

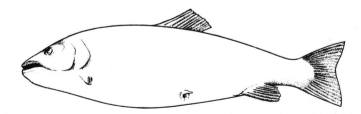

Fig. 129. The cast ready for painting (the paired fins will be attached later)

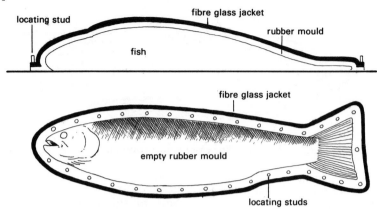

Fig. 130. Moulding a fish in rubber

set fairly quickly. The first coat should always be applied to fins which have been soaked in acetone. This will allow the resin to penetrate into the 'fabric' of the fin and thus bind solidly to it. With this method there will be little chance of the resin separating from the fin to produce light patches, such as are seen in many specimens embedded in clear resin. The fins after each coating are placed in an upright position, so that excess resin can run off to the cut end of the fin, where the drops may later be removed. (This is a particularly useful method with very thin membraneous fins as the transparency is retained.)

Once the fins are prepared (by either method) they are now stored for addition to the cast after it has been painted. Their addition to the cast before painting would only make the job of painting more complicated.

MOULDING IN RUBBER

This method of preparing the positive cast of a fish has proved very successful. However, the plaster cast presents certain problems. First, it is rigid and the mould must be broken in order to remove it from the fibre-glass form. Secondly, only one specimen can be made. A rubber material, although much more expensive, would make the mould flexible and enable more than one fibre-glass cast to be produced. The use of rubber will also enable one to cast more of the fish specimen.

Wacker Silicon from Micro Products is an excellent rubber to use. Layers of this can be built up on the fish and then reinforced with fine muslin or strips cut from nylon stockings. A quarter-of-an-inch of rubber will be sufficient as a fibre-glass outer casing will be required to add rigidity. The rubber moulding around the fish must be keyed into the fibre-glass jacket. This is best done by first making a tube of stiff card about the thickness of a pencil, then pouring rubber into the tube and leaving it upright until dry. The long rubber form can now be cut into one-inch lengths and stuck to the rubber edge of the fish mould with wet rubber and held in place with a pin. The pin is removed when the rubber lug is dry and firmly attached.

When applying the outer casing over the rubber mould, the fibre-glass should be allowed to run around these locating lugs so that when dry the rubber mould can be detached from the fibre-glass jacket.

To reproduce a fish, a gel-coat resin is painted onto the inside of the rubber mould. It is possible to tint the gel-coat as required. Allow this first coat to become tacky and then add ordinary lay-up resin stippled over matting to add strength. The cast should be built up to the thickness required and allowed to dry thoroughly. To release the fish cast from the mould the outer jacket must be removed. The rubber mould can now be peeled off gently and replaced in the fibre-glass jacket with the locating lugs fitted into place, ready to receive more gel-coat to produce another fish cast.

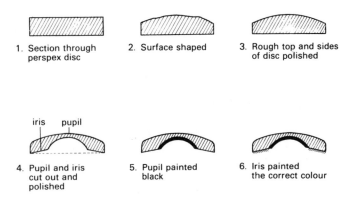

1. Section through perspex disc

2. Surface shaped

3. Rough top and sides of disc polished

iris   pupil

4. Pupil and iris cut out and polished

5. Pupil painted black

6. Iris painted the correct colour

Fig. 131. Making fish eyes

The fins, which have been moulded in a similar way, are also produced in resin and later attached to the fish cast in their natural positions. The cast is now trimmed and cleaned. A wooden block is fitted into the back of the cast and held in place with resin. This block will secure the fish to its back-board. All that remains is for the eye to be fitted and the fish to be painted.

MAKING AN ARTIFICIAL EYE

The eye must now be considered. If the species being cast is not of the bug-eyed variety it is possible to paint the eye on to the surface if this is of correct shape. Such an eye, well painted, can look extremely natural after several coats of clear varnish and should certainly look much more natural than most proprietory fish eyes available today. The only alternative to such an eye, and the only one open in the case of species with greatly curved protruding eyes, is to make an eye of correct outer surface and colour for the species. Since shaping and polishing are involved, both for the outer and inner (concave) surface representing the pupil, perspex is probably the best material to use. When using an artificial eye, it should be slightly larger than the surface diameter of the actual eye. This is cut out of the cast, exactly to shape. The hole left is shaped to receive the artificial eye without altering the actual outline of the eye cut from the mould. The artificial eye is inserted from

the rear and held in position with filler paste such as was used in modelling alterations to the cast. When painting the perspex eye, only oil colours should be used, as cellulose paints cause 'crazing' of the perspex because of the attack on the material by the paint solvents.

PAINTING THE CAST

As mentioned earlier, this is the most difficult part of the whole exercise. Success here depends very much on the painting skill of the individual. A good colour sense and experience in 'handling' colours are essential if the final object produced is to bear any resemblance, not only in shape but also in colour, to the original.

To begin with, colour references of the fish are essential, for the time between seeing the fish and having the cast ready for painting is usually long enough to cloud the memory of any individual. Colour notes, i.e. colour sketches of the whole and parts of the fish, should only be used by the person who originally produced them from the fish, since no two individuals see the same colour in the same way. More useful and meaningful are coloured photographs of the fish, as long as these include some object of known colour – at best, for example, a colour reference strip such as is produced by Kodak.

Comparison of the colour reference object in the photographs with the original will show the true colours in the photo-

115

graph, i.e. they may be too red or too blue, so that corrections can be made. The chance to take photographs of the whole fish as well as details of scaling, fins and other important aspects, should therefore never be passed up. Bright, diffused light, rather than intense sun or artificial light, should be used, so that the fish shows few if any highlights which could be mistaken for areas of white colour, or at best would obscure detail, structure and colour.

Though each individual fish or species requires its own procedure because of its own characteristics, it is possible to give a few hints on painting a cast.

Obviously once the cast has been painted, it should not look as though it has been painted. There should be no visible brush marks. The coats of paint should be as thin as possible, so as not to obscure detail of scaling and fin structure (after the trouble that was taken during moulding to pick them up). Areas of colour should never be separated from each other by hard edges, but should always grade into each other, even if only over a very short distance. This is achieved by spray rather than by brushpainting. Spray-guns of various sizes, including small ones called airbrushes, are available. If you have to use paintbrushes, use only those of the best quality, such as sable brushes.

Spray application will limit use to the cellulose or acrylic based paints. These have great covering power and only a thin layer need be applied, so that details of the structure on the cast will not be obscured. These paints, which are readily available from car repair establishments, can be easily diluted with various organic solvents such as acetone or ethyl acetate. In their most dilute form they can readily be applied as tones to produce subtle overtones in any shade. Their rapid drying will allow the application of successive coats with little or no delay.

Their only disadvantage is that the painted surface may be disturbed if some paint is applied by brush. But this can be overcome by using a high-boiling-point (slow–evaporating) solvent such as butyl acetate or petroleum ether as a solvent for the paint to be applied by brush.

Before you actually undertake any painting, you should become familiar with the colour structure of fish. If you remove the scales from part of a fish you will find that the pigment of the fish is actually carried in its skin, and that the only pigment carried by the scales is silver. The scaleless part has retained much of its colour, though this is less bright.

This structuring can readily be reproduced by initially painting the cast to the skin colour of the species with dark-back grading to light-belly over the flanks. The scales are then individually painted, using a paint actually containing the silver material extracted from scales (pearl-essence). Several coats of this paint may have to be applied to each scale to produce the required depth of silver. This will actually allow the gradation of silver found over the surface of a scale to be reproduced by varying the area covered by each coat. The scales, once painted, can be oversprayed to produce the gradual change from dark-back to silver flanks to white belly and underside.

After the cast has been painted, all that remains is to add the pectoral and pelvic fins. The fins, whether casts or dried, will already have been coloured up as required. Once they have been properly fitted they can be 'glued' into position with body-filler. This can be used also to model the joint, which is then painted.

Several coats of non-darkening varnish of a non–cellulose base compatible with the paints used will give a realistic 'wet look' to the cast.

16

Reptiles, Amphibians and Crustaceans

It may be necessary at some stage to prepare reptiles, amphibians and crustaceans for display. This can be done in one of three ways. First, you can prepare them by freeze-drying – which is by far the best method, as freeze-drying retains the natural colours of the specimen. Secondly, you can prepare them by casting and moulding, producing the specimen in plaster or plastic and ultimately painting on its natural colours. The third method is skinning. The specimen is skinned and mounted in the same way as has been described for most specimens of natural history. After being dried thoroughly, it is painted and set into a natural habitat. If a freeze-drier is not available, I suggest that you prepare this group as follows:

SNAKES

Very small specimens are best cast in plaster or wax. Larger ones can be skinned.

Lay the dead snake on a piece of white paper and do a touch drawing of it in its required position. An incision approximately one-and-a-half inches long is made in the centre of the underside of the body. The skin is loosened all around the incision and as far round the circumference of the body as possible. The body is cut completely in half. Every effort must be made not, in any circumstances, to cut the skin itself. With the two halves of the body free, each can be pulled from the skin, rather as fingers are extracted from a glove. When the skull is reached, the main body bulk is removed and the skull cleaned of eyes, brain and all flesh. Extract the other half of the body as far as the vent and cut this half

of the body free.

The flesh of the tail – that is to say, from the vent to the tip of the tail – will not come out from the inside. Therefore a further incision must be made on the underside of this part of the body and the tail extracted. The empty skin is now cleaned of fat and flesh and preserved. Montagu Browne's soap-based preservative mentioned on p. 27 is best for this job.

Mounting

Begin to stitch from the tip of the tail towards the vent, leaving a gap large enough to fill this part with fine damp sawdust or sand. Now fill the tail to capacity and block off the main body area with a piece of cotton-wool, which will prevent the sawdust or sand from falling out. Complete the tail part and stitch up to the vent. The damp sawdust can now be put through the belly incision a little at a time and tamped firmly into position with the aid of a piece of dowel or even a long pencil. Fill up the belly opening. Attention must now be turned to the forward end of the skin. Fill the cranium and base of the skull with some soft modelling compound and then continue to fill the rest of the skin with the damp sawdust. On reaching the centre of the body, fill and tamp the sawdust until it is completely full but not so full that the skin bulges unnaturally. Place a small piece of soft cloth over the sawdust inside the skin and sew the two edges of the skin together; the cloth will prevent the sawdust from falling out while stitching. The snake can now be turned over and the rest of the head modelled, the mouth being closed firmly by pinning and the correct eyes fitted. Place the specimen on to the touch drawing and adjust for length and shape. Prop the snake into the required attitude and leave until dry. When dry, paint with oil colours.

A slightly better method is as follows:

Position the snake on a flat surface, e.g. a piece of glass, and make a mould of the reptile in plaster. When the plaster is dry, remove the snake's body and put the mould on one side to dry thoroughly. Prepare the snake for skinning. Skin the snake by making a full-length incision along the body. Free the skin and remove the carcass. Clean and preserve the skin as before. The skin is now stored until a cast has been made from the mould of the snake. Having made the cast as described above, in Chapter 15, simply stick the skin over the plaster form of the snake and when dry paint it. It is always a good idea, when dealing with fish, reptiles, amphibians or crustaceans, the most difficult of subjects to prepare by normal taxidermy methods, to take colour photographs to aid in the final painting.

FROGS AND LIZARDS

Smaller specimens are best cast in plaster or wax or celluloid, using a gelatine or cold rubber mould. The larger specimens, however, are mostly prepared like mammals. Lizards are skinned through the ventral incision and the four limbs extracted in the same way as described for smaller mammals. The skull is left in the skin but must be thoroughly cleaned of all fat and flesh. The preserved skin has a thin coat of modelling compound laid inside and the artificial body is put in place. The four limbs are wired exactly as for mammals. After the skin of the incision has been sewn together, the specimen is placed on its temporary base and patted all over with a flat paddle-like stick in order to shape and model it. After drying, the specimen is fitted with the correct eyes and the skin is painted.

Frogs are best skinned through the mouth, which leaves no ugly stitches in view. By opening the large mouth wide, a fine pair of scissors can be used to sever the neck vertebrae just below the base of the skull. By careful manipulation the shoulders can be exposed sufficiently to be cut and released too. The body can now be extracted, and finally the rear limbs can be cut free. Each limb should be pulled inside out in turn and cleaned. After preserving, fine tow can be wound around the limb bones, which are then covered in modelling compound, and the skin filled either with damp sawdust or with sand. In my own experience, modelling compound of the correct consistency is far better than the loose-filled method. Positioning and modelling are much easier, and when dry the specimen is much more robust. Finally, short sharp wires are pushed up each limb and the specimen is secured to its temporary base until dry. Once dry, the specimen is painted.

TURTLES

Turtles are probably best mounted rather than cast. In order to remove the body, the plastron or under-shell can be neatly sawn from the upper-shell at the side columns which join it to the upper-shell. When these have been sawn through, the plastron will hang until the skin around the back limbs and tail are cut as close to the body as possible. *Do not* cut the skin around the front limbs and the neck, but allow the plastron to hang free, using the front skin as a hinge. The main body bulk is easily removed, and all four limbs and the tail are skinned as with smaller mammals. The neck is also inverted and cut off at the base of the skull, which must stay in place as the skin of the head is firmly attached. After being thoroughly cleaned, the whole specimen should be washed and placed in a weak salt brine solution of two pints of warm water to six ounces of salt. The final preservative should be a soap-based one. To mount the specimen, follow the method described for smaller mammals, by first making an artificial body in wood-wool. The neck and all the limbs should be on wires and the bone coverings covered finally in soft modelling compound, which will facilitate the ultimate modelling of the wrinkles in the skin.

CRUSTACEANS

These include lobsters, crayfish and crabs. Their skeletons are, of course, external in the form of the bony armour. When dealing with sizeable specimens, it is best to detach all limbs from their attachments to the body. With hooked wires, all flesh can now be extracted. The inside of the main body can also be cleaned out and the whole specimen washed thoroughly in running water.

To preserve the specimen, immerse it in a dilute solution of 2 per cent formalin for two to three hours. Remove from the preservative and wash thoroughly. The inside of the creature should now be painted with the glycerine solution mentioned on p. 27. This will ensure that the ligaments at the joints are kept soft and flexible to aid subsequent modelling.

Soft galvanised wires are cut and fitted into each limb. These are now filled with a good-quality modelling compound or papier-mâché. The inside of the body is also filled with papier-mâché, and the limbs are attached in their natural positions. The limb wires protruding from the upper ends of the limbs are simply stuck into the stiffer papier-mâché of the body. The specimen is now positioned and modelled up. It may be necessary to support the body of some specimens until dry. It is important to make sure that the leg wires do not protrude from the foot of all limbs, but there may be one on each side with which the specimen is secured to its display base.

17

Freeze–Drying Small Vertebrates, Fungi and Flowers

To the professional preparator the preservation of natural history specimens by the method of freeze-drying may appear, to say the least, to be cheating. The quality of the results, however, and the applicability of the technique to hitherto unpreservable and difficult material more than compensates for this.

Dehydration from the frozen state – 'freeze-drying' – is a well-established procedure in the pharmaceutical industry for the preparation of soluble drugs, and in medical research for the preparation of histological specimens. In histology, freeze-drying permits the preparation of a dehydrated tissue specimen which has not been subjected to fixatives which can seriously alter the integrity of the chemical components of the cells. From the small single organ freeze-dried for microscopic study, to the complete animal prepared for museum display, it involves relatively minor modifications in technique and equipment.

Freeze-drying involves the removal of water from the tissue solution and its concentration into ice crystals which can be regarded as foreign bodies. Freezing is really dehydration in which the water is isolated locally in the tissue rather than being completely removed. About 90 to 95 per cent of the water in any tissue will freeze, so dehydration by freezing is not complete. But the water that remains is chemically involved with the tissue components. The tissue looks and feels dry.

The rate at which the specimen is frozen will determine the size of the ice crystals formed. Slow rates of freezing, such as would be obtained in an ordinary deep-freeze, will make these crystals grow to

many times the size of the cells. These crystals, however, appear to be exclusively extracellular. As they grow, they remove water from both intracellular and extracellular locations, and the cells collapse passively into the interstices between the ice crystals. H.T. Merryman, a specialist in freeze-drying, explains that this does not appear to damage the cells. The source of injury to frozen cells appears to be the effect of dehydration rather than the physical presence of crystals.

When the freezing rate is increased, the ice crystals are smaller and their number correspondingly greater. With extremely high rates of freezing the tendency for extracellular crystal formation is overwhelmed and the crystals appear within the cells. Merryman and Kafig suggest that tissues subjected to this high rate of freezing do not survive, except for red blood cells, which are atypical both because of their small size lack of internal structure.

Harris showed in 1954 that if cellular material is allowed to dry at room temperature severe shrinkage results. The material becomes relatively insoluble, radical changes in the chemical make-up take place and the cells are irreversibly injured. The technique of freeze-drying was developed with the hope of preventing these alterations.

The technique of freeze-drying consists basically of freezing the specimens, and its rate depends on the vapour pressure of water in the atmosphere surrounding the specimen.

Freeze-drying is subdivided into three main stages. The first is the conversion of ice to vapour, which occurs at a rate dependent upon the temperature of the ice crystals.

Where histological detail is required the drying is usually done at −30 °C, or even lower. Higher temperatures allow ice crystals to grow in size through a transfer of water from the smaller crystals to the larger ones.

The second stage is the removal of the water vapour from the specimen to the surrounding atmosphere. The transfer occurs by simple gaseous diffusion and its rate depends on the vapour pressure of water in the atmosphere surrounding the specimen. The principal aim of the freeze-drying unit is to maintain as low a water vapour pressure as possible.

The third stage is the removal of the water from the atmosphere. This used to be done by simply exposing the specimen to a relatively high vacuum. But recently a method has been described by Merryman in which drying can be carried out at atmospheric pressure by passing very dry air over the specimen to sweep away the water vapour.

It has become apparent that there is a general relationship between body weight and the length of drying time. This relationship is affected both by the permeability of the epidermis and by the water content within the specimen.

Approximate drying times

Specimen	Species	Time in days
small passerine	*Acanthis flammea*	8-9
small mammal	*Muridae*	8-10
reptile, amphibian	*Bufo bufo*	8-10
flower	*Amaryllidaceae*	2-3
fungi	*Agaricineae*	2-3

Specimens will come to no harm if left in the freeze-drier for a few days longer than estimated. Specimens which have been eviscerated will dry much more quickly.

PREPARING THE SPECIMEN

Eyes

Before the specimen can be set in its natural position, before freezing, the eyes should be removed. This is done simply by inserting fine pointed forceps deep into the corner of the eye and grasping the optic nerve at the back of the eye. Removed correctly, the eye-sockets should be quite dry and the correct eyes can now be inserted. The wire on the back of the eye can be pushed into the skull and the lids pulled over the eyes in their original positions.

I have found that the fixing of glass eyes into mammals and birds is much better than painting the cornea, which remains as a thin structure over the eye and appears white and opaque. The glass eye is, of course, much stronger. For reptiles and amphibians, however, the painting of the cornea is by far the better method, as the eyes fit so tightly to the paper-thin lids.

Posing the specimen

In the initial stages of freeze-drying the final positioning of specimens was a difficult problem. The technique of freezing the joints of limbs, neck and backbone was employed. The agent used was liquid nitrogen. This odourless non-toxic gas is available in liquid form and is simply applied to the joints, which are frozen into the required position. Liquid nitrogen evaporates rapidly, leaving no trace of wetness or oiliness such as would be produced by any other liquid coolant. Despite its very low temperature it is not hazardous to use. If it is accidentally splashed on to the skin it boils so readily that the skin is hardly cooled. I feel that the best method of positioning, say, a small bird or a small mammal, e.g. a mouse, is by the use of wires. (Freshly killed mice are much easier to set up than mice that have spent some time in the deep-freeze.) A thin, but strong, wire is pushed up the vent and guided up the underside of the cervical vertebrae through the skull and out through one of the nostrils. Care must be taken to see that the wire is in this described position, or it will give an unnatural shape to the specimen when finally positioned. Secure the specimen by means of this wire to a piece of balsa wood. Never use thin polystyrene as it will curl and distort during drying. The rear feet of the mouse can now be pinned to give the impression that they are carrying the weight of the animal. Many specimens are spoilt by the toes looking flat and unnatural. You can now bend the mouse into the chosen position, pinning the front feet down if the specimen is to be on all fours. Use small thin pins and push the pin-heads down onto the feet, so that they will not interfere with the natural bend of the limbs. Arrange the tail, and cross-pin it to hold it in position. Finally, check that the mouth is closed, and with a fine paintbrush comb the fur down evenly.

Initial freezing

Specimens should be placed in a conventional deep-freeze until sufficiently frozen before being placed in the freeze-drier. Twelve hours is the minimum time, but I recommend twenty-four to be quite sure. Botanical specimens can take even longer, as they appear to be quite resistant to low temperatures. R. H. Harris instructed me to place flowers after freezing into a beaker containing a little liquid nitrogen and then to place beaker and flowers in to the EF2 for drying; the liquid nitrogen gives the lower temperature necessary for plant tissue.

With some specimens, especially those that have been frozen for long periods, it may be necessary to inject a mixture of water and glycerine to fill out hollows. After the specimen has been frozen in the deep-freeze it should be taken out and pricked with a needle all over its body, especially along the underside of the tail. This procedure enables the water vapour to reach the surface of the specimen evenly, thus minimising shrinkage.

The dryness of specimens is monitored by periodically weighing them until a constant weight is reached. The weighing apparatus should be placed in the commercial freezer so that there is little chance of the specimens thawing, thus preventing condensation of moisture.

Preservation of completed specimens

It would be reasonable to assume that specimens preserved in the way already described would absorb moisture from the air quite readily and would ultimately decompose. Surprisingly enough, this is not the case. Specimens preserved by freeze-drying, simply kept under normal atmospheric conditions, have survived for many years without added precautions of air conditioning or humidity control. It has also been suggested that these completed specimens are impervious to parasitic pests.

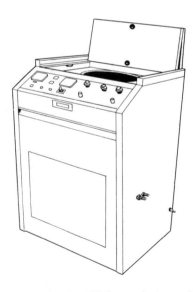

Fig. 132. The EF2 freeze-drying unit

However, I can state categorically that the larvae of the bread beetle *Stegobium paniceum* will certainly relish and survive on such tasty morsels. Specimens to be maintained in an environment such as a museum, where this contamination might be expected, would certainly need to be poisoned in some way for their protection.

Colour

The colour of both fur and feather is quite unaltered. Amphibians also retain good colour, as do caterpillars. In my experience, reptiles usually change colour slightly. So too do a number of small freshwater fishes.

Flowers that I have seen prepared by R. H. Harris have retained excellent colour, but he informs me that they become very brittle and fragile and have a life of no more than one or two years.

According to Merryman, taxidermists generally feel that freeze-drying is a short cut to their art. This has not been my experience, as most taxidermists welcome the technique and find it an extremely useful one when setting up small mammals. It eliminates the need for casting or borax drying of fungi and eases the difficulties encountered when preparing reptiles and amphibians. In fact only a well-trained and experienced taxidermist will achieve good results when setting up and freeze-drying specimens of natural history.

18

Preparing Skeletons

The preparation of complete skeletons of vertebrates with their bones cleaned, degreased and fixed into a natural position, i.e. 'mounted', is to say the least a highly skilled craft, which is practised only by a few. The work is divided into two main stages: (a) the preparation of all the bones, and (b) the articulation of the skeleton.

PREPARATION

The viscera, skin and muscles can be removed from the bones, but before the bones are clean enough to store or mount, special techniques are necessary. The treatment prescribed must not be severe, or the bones will become soft, chalky and fragile.

Completed bones should be free from natural grease, and must be white and firm. The exact treatment to be used depends largely on the type of animal and the conditions under which the work is to be done.

Before assembling the skeleton, you must have an elementary knowledge of bones. Detailed knowledge of some of the bones can be gained from various osteological and anatomical textbooks. The thorough cleaning of bones and the building of the skeleton to its natural position is a skill that all taxidermists should learn. Parts of the skeleton are used in most preparations, and an understanding of exactly how a skeleton is put together is invaluable, and helps one to appreciate the bird or mammal more fully. Before attempting to carry out any osteological work, there are certain factors that we must be aware of and certain data that must be collected.

1. The animal must be seen while alive, freshly killed or recently out of the deep-freeze. It must be identified and sexed correctly.

2. The label you give the specimen *must* stay attached and be legible until preparation is complete.

3. Ideally the total weight, height at rump and shoulder and, for small mammals, total length, head and body length and hind foot length should be taken when the animal is fresh.

4. Do not run the risk of catching disease. Weil's disease can be caught from the brown rat and possibly from the urine of a large number of other wild and domestic species – by mouth or through breaks in the skin. Anthrax, tuberculosis and brucellosis are the other major hazards. Anthrax can of course also be caught from material which has been buried. Rodents and hedgehogs may carry salmonellosis (see Appendix 2). Unless the animal has been passed fit for human consumption or checked by a veterinarian there may be risks, but the main thing is to avoid using domestic animals that have died mysteriously. While preparing material, avoid hand-to-mouth operations, such as smoking. Cover any cuts in the skin, and wear rubber gloves and the protective clothing that you keep at your place of work. Afterwards wash up to your elbows in soap and warm water (paying attention to the fingernails) and sterilise any instruments or equipment you use by boiling or soaking in phenol or cetavlon solutions of the correct strength. Remember to burn all rubbish.

METHODS USED TO CLEAN BONES

There are many methods which can be employed when cleaning and whitening bones. Maceration is probably the first method used in preparing bones and skeletons. Whole carcasses left in the open to rot of their own accord can often produce good results. Maceration can be done under controlled conditions with the use of tanks and water.

The specimen to be macerated is submerged in warm water and a cube of rotting flesh added. The progress of maceration must be checked daily.

Skeletons to be completed as articulated should be extracted before the cartilage has decomposed. Maceration certainly has its drawbacks, as skeletons prepared in this way will produce foul lingering smells. The tanks in which the skeletons are prepared must therefore be sealed with tight-fitting lids.

Enzymes

There are few enzymatic practices used in the preparation of bones; the one which I find sufficient for my needs is papaine. With small specimens, fleshing is not really essential. Larger specimens, however, should have the viscera removed and the flesh taken from the bones.

The tank to be used should be filled with hot water (50-60 °C), and the papaine added at a rate of 0.05 gm per 100 cc of water. Place the specimen to be cleaned into the tank and incubate it for some twenty-four hours, keeping the mixture at a constant temperature. Small mammals, such as the mouse and mole, should be macerated at a temperature of between 50-60 °C (120-160 °F). These will be completed in eight to ten hours. The papaine solution can be used time and time again. In fact the older the solution the more efficient its properties are. Any bottom sediment should be removed and disposed of periodically.

Incubating papaine has a foul smell and should be done in an area which has a direct outward draught, e.g. a fume cupboard. Keep specimens in containers which have tight-fitting lids and so avoid the escape of fumes when the specimens are not in use.

Specimens prepared in papaine generally do not require degreasing, but they should be bleached and the bones air-dried on completion.

Note that if specimens are left in the papaine solution for too long they will become extremely fragile and will be of little use for either mounting or disarticulated preparations. Constant vigilance is therefore necessary when using this enzyme.

Pancreatin is a very useful preparation for most small skeletons, with the exception of fish and some amphibians. Skin, flesh and remove the viscera from the specimen, leaving all the limbs and the skull attached to the cartilage. Transfer the specimen to a suitable container to which is added a modification of the American taxidermist John Rowley's fluid, formulated as follows:

sodium sulphide	1 gm
pancreatin	2 gm
normal saline	1000 cc

The saline solution is made in accordance with the specimen to be prepared. Mammal saline should be 0.9 per cent NaCl in distilled water, avian and reptilian 0.75 per cent and amphibian 0.65 per cent (R. H. Harris, *Museum Journal* 58).

The specimen should now be allowed to simmer gently in the solution. The time allowed will depend on the size of the animal, and on whether it is fresh or has been preserved. After some twenty or thirty minutes remove the specimen and check for signs of maceration. When the flesh on the bones is seen to fall away quite easily, stop the process and transfer the specimen to a bowl of clean water. The loose flesh can now be picked, scraped or brushed from the bones until they are clean. A solution of chloride of lime will be found useful in the removing of stubborn tissue. The solution should be of a creamy consistency and brushed over the bones affected.

If the skeleton requires bleaching, now is the time to do it. Immerse the skeleton for approximately one hour in a solution of twenty volumes of hydrogen peroxide with a trace of ammonium hydroxide. This bleaching agent can be used several times. If it is necessary to degrease the specimen, use one of the following degreasing agents: undiluted acetone, benzine, xylene or chloroform (see p. 131).

The now clean specimen is ready to be set

up in its natural position. Cork sheets are most useful for this part of the operation. The skeleton is still pliable and can be orientated over the cork sheet. Pins are used to secure the toes, and pieces of cork to support the skull and limbs until the specimen is dry. It is not necessary to wire the bones, as they have been kept together throughout the treatment. When dry, the cartilage will give all the support required. To dry the specimen, put it in an airy place and cover it to prevent fluff and dust from adhering to the bones, until it is thoroughly dry.

Antiformin

Antiformin is extensively used in bacteriology for breaking down mucin and similar tissue. It is found particularly suitable when preparing small skulls and postcranial elements from material that has been preserved in formaldehyde or alcohol for long periods. When preparing the antiformin solution the necessary ingredients are as follows:

sodium carbonate	150 gm
bleaching powder	100 gm
water	1000 cc

Put the sodium carbonate in 250 cc of water, and add the bleaching powder to the remaining 750 cc. Mix the two solutions thoroughly by shaking for approximately three minutes. When mixed, filter, and add to the filtrate an equal quantity of 15 per cent sodium hydroxide in distilled water.

The specimens are immersed in the antiformin solution for a few hours. They should have been washed previously in running water. Check the specimens hourly. When there are signs of maceration the bones can be scraped or brushed to remove the tissue. A jet of gently running warm water can be directed on to the tissue in order to wash it away from the bone. Delicate and fragile elements, such as ear ossicles and teeth, usually remain attached to their points of origin. As de-fatting is not necessary with this technique, the bones can be bleached and air-dried to complete the task.

Sodium perborate

1. Having fully removed the skin, clean off the flesh (only rough fleshing is done in the case of delicate specimens), remove the tongue and wash out some of the brain with a jet of water. Macerate, or a slow, long simmer first but *do not boil vigorously*.

2. Soak in cold water for twenty-four hours to remove blood. A longer soaking will enable maceration to begin and the specimen will smell.

3. Place bones in a suitable container according to size – jam-jar, plastic bucket or a plastic dustbin. Pack bones loosely to fill the container half-full.

4. Use up to 60–100 gm sodium perborate powder per litre of boiling water. It can be bought in 500 gm bottles from any chemical supplier or in 50 kg bags – not quite so fresh. The water must cover the bones, and they will need to be wedged down if they float, e.g. with a stout piece of card or a slate. The perborate must be tetrahydiate and fresh (i.e. there must be vigorous effervescence when boiling water is added). This can be difficult, especially with bulk purchase. You must test the recipe and send it back to source if it is not found to be fresh.

Perborate forms a dilute peroxide solution in sodium borate, which is slightly alkaline. It does not damage bones, and they can be left in it almost indefinitely. In fact the bones go on whitening, if they are left.

5. Put the powder on to the skeleton, spread it well and put a little into the foramen magnum. Do not allow the powder to become damp, as this will make it react less violently. *Immediately pour boiling water on to the dry powder and bones*. If you cannot boil enough water in one go, do half and come back later with more boiling water. Swish the contents to ensure that all the powder reacts – experiment will soon show how much is needed.

6. Tie a polythene cover over the container as soon as the water is added. Do not use a screw cap or the jar will explode. Vast quantities of oxygen are being released and must be kept in contact with the bone while the action is occurring. Stand the container in a sink or outdoors.

7. Once the bubbles have subsided and the water is cooled you can remove the lid and, if you cannot deal with the bones at once, allow the water gradually to evaporate. An odourless, dry skeleton surrounded by crystals results and this can be left without damage for weeks. To re-work, soak in hot water.

8. Clean the white flesh off the bones, taking care not to lose small bones and epiphyses, as everything is now the same colour. Go through any flesh carefully before you discard. If you know the anatomy of the species the process is rapid and bones can be scrubbed with a nailbrush or a tooth-brush. Plenty of detergent and hot water at this stage gets out a lot of the grease.

9. Spread the skeleton on newspaper in a tray with a label firmly attached – preferably to a bone – and allow to dry. For archaeological work, bones are best separated. You can keep the bones of each limb in a separately labelled container. If you want an articulated skeleton give lighter treatment and cut through the tendons, especially under the paws, or they will contract and pull the bones out of joint.

10. Bones can be degreased if necessary. Long bones of larger than hare size may need a hole drilled at each end and wire pushed right through to make a hole the length of the bone. Avoid diagnostic regions when drilling holes! Soaking in 10 per cent commercial ammonia (for a fortnight) is recommended for greasy bones with a final clean in a commercial solution of Eau de Javel (one part E.d.J. and one part water). In Britain this may be difficult to obtain – substitute Deosan Blue Label, 1.5 per cent available chlorine. Peroxide should be avoided, as it eventually damages the bone.

Notes

1. There is no need to 'skin' an animal and dissect it in the usual way. If you know how a mammal skeleton is organised you can, for example:

(a)   flesh and remove the skull – separate the atlas from the condyles of the skull

(b)   flesh and remove the fore-limbs and scapula (only muscle holds most scapulae to the rib cage but in some, look for a collar bone — it may be very small)

(c)   flesh and remove the hind-limbs – separate the head of the femur from the acetabulum of the pelvis

(d)   Remove the fur, flesh and viscera from the remainder and divide the vertebral column and pelvis that remains into two or three sections by removing some ribs from the sternum and finding raised parts where the centre of the vertebrae meet

2. Although dissecting instruments are useful, a good sharp kitchen knife is adequate for most of the work. A large catering firm will provide non-stainless steel boning knives which keep a better edge, if you wish to prepare large specimens.

3. Stages 1–9 in the perborate section are usually enough for most quick reference material and perborate can also be used to whiten old bone.

4. A gentle simmer can be given *before* the perborate stage. If you simmer afterwards, you can damage the bone and pit the container. Ideally 'cooking' should be avoided, but a simmer or a slight maceration before perborate will save a lot of labour at the joints of a skeleton. Many odd tendons will disappear to a dry wisp, however, when the skeleton is left to dry.

5. If you intend to simmer, it is essential to remove some of the brain, or it may push the cranial bones apart. To prevent teeth being pulled out of their sockets when mucous membranes shrink, make a careful cut through these membranes and the underlying tissue from back to front of the palate on the roof of the mouth and similar cuts alongside teeth rows in the mandibles. If you are not fleshing completely before simmering, make sure that large muscle masses are cut at right angles to their direction of pull, or they may contract on cooking and pull off epiphyses or small processes.

6. The skeleton number or name should go on each bone in waterproof ink when the skeleton is really dry, as people using collections often put bones back in the wrong box by mistake. Cover the number with dilute resin solution to prevent greasy hands wearing it off.

MACERATION OF SMALL SPECIMENS

We will assume that after maceration the skeleton will be mounted for display. First and foremost it must be stressed that small skeletons are delicate and must be handled with extreme care.

The specimen is first skinned and its organs and as much tissue as possible removed. The joints should not be disarticulated. In fact the joint ligaments should be preserved where possible.

When the specimen is free of tissue, it is best placed in a beaker, preferably glass, and a 2 per cent solution of potassium hydroxide added. The solution is then heated to about 60 °C (140 °F). Sodium peroxide is another useful agent in which to simmer bones. When the solution has discoloured, which usually takes some thirty minutes, the skeleton should be examined and further tissue removed.

Some bones may well become detached during this process. They can be dealt with in the usual way, however. If the specimen is not sufficiently macerated, a continuation of the process with fresh solution is necessary. The two known dangers of potassium peroxide are a tendency for joint ligaments to curl and a rapid softening. Both these conditions can be avoided by examining the specimen frequently. If in any doubt as to whether the specimen is becoming too soft or the tissues are beginning to curl, turn off the heat and continue to clean by hand.

Small animals usually require little or no degreasing, but prolonged washing will eventually remove any grease. Bleaching is all that is left to be done. Five to ten volumes of hydrogen peroxide should be used, and the specimen can be left in this solution for a day or two before supporting it in its natural mounting position. Cottons can be used to support the bones, suspending them from retort stands like a puppet.

Forced drying, i.e. by means of a hair-drier or on top of a radiator, will not harm the specimen, providing it does not get too hot. If, after drying, you find that some of the joints have not set in the correct posi-tions, a simple relaxing process can be carried out. Simply soak in water by wrapping wet cotton-wool around the joint until it is supple. Reset into the required position.

MACERATION OF LARGER SPECIMENS

The specimen should be skinned and the viscera removed, in the same way as for the smaller specimens. Fore-legs and hind-legs should be removed. The skull should also be removed and the brain extracted. All muscles and cartilage should be removed, but scraping at this stage is not necessary.

Cloth bags should now be prepared; stockinette is the ideal material. The various bones should be placed in the bags and the whole thing put into the macerating tank. A string attached to each bag will enable the contents to be examined without fuss. The heat can be switched on and a simmering temperature of between 60 °C (140 °F) and 70 °C (150 °F) attained. Constant vigilance is required to ensure that the bones do not become too soft and the tank does not boil dry. In the case of large specimens, simmering can take days.

Into the macerating tank should be placed some sodium perborate (see perborate method). Specimens will not be harmed if left stored in the perborate until work can begin on them.

The end of the process is indicated when all adherent tissues come away from the bones with a gentle scraping. Also, all remaining periosteum should be removed.

The skull

The skull will need special attention. All the remaining brain tissue will have to be thoroughly swilled out through the foramen magnum.

After completing the bone cleaning process, all bones will be ready for the next stage. If at all possible the skull should be washed in running water for a day or two. This process is, of course, a preliminary to degreasing.

Long bones

Long bones can be difficult to degrease. To facilitate this, a small hole one-sixteenth of an inch in diameter can be drilled in either end of the bone. Drill the holes as near to the centre of the ends as possible, so as not to destroy any bone markings. The drill should pass into the centre of the bone, running parallel with its length. Place the bones back into running water and from time to time they can be taken out and shaken in much the same way as the shaking of a whip or axe. The degreasing agents widely used are carbon tetrachloride or trichlorethylene. Greasy bones should be immersed for three to five hours. Bones so immersed should not lie in their own discarded grease but should be supported on a wire frame, which will allow the grease to fall to the bottom of the tank.

When degreasing has been completed, the bones should be laid on clean blotting paper until dry.

To complete the process, bleaching is required. This is done by immersing the bones in a solution of 5-10 volumes of hydrogen peroxide. Bones should stay in the solution for one or two days. Care must be taken not to leave the bones in the solution for too long; otherwise they will become soft, chalky and useless.

PREPARING FISH SKELETONS

The preparation of fish skeletons is fairly straightforward if the correct procedures are followed. Frozen fish make the best specimens for the beginner to start on, as freezing is said to break down some constituents of the tissues, so making it easier to scrape them from the bones.

Skin your specimen carefully, making sure that no bones are cut or removed. I suggest that a half to one-inch strip of skin be left adhering to the perimeter of the specimen. This will hold the median fins in position and give support to the paired fins. It is at the next stage that prior knowledge of the fish skeleton is invaluable.

Rough out and remove as much of the soft tissue as is possible. When scraping the individual bones always scrape from their ends to the middle. In this way there is less likelihood of cutting through the cartilage holding one bone to another. To loosen these ligaments at this stage can be disastrous.

Begin your cleaning from the head end first. This is a fairly robust area and not as delicately articulated as the rest of the skeleton. The removal of the gill structure is achieved by cutting from the mandible those membranes which lie on either side of the hyoid member that supports the tongue. Follow the gill-arch and cut through the attachment between the suspensory phatingeal and the inner anterior surface of the operculum. The next incision should be made on each side, and at the posterior end of the urohyal, cutting the attachment of the urohyal at the clavicles. The operation should be done most carefully, and if done correctly the gill-arch should be almost free, but for its remaining dorsal attachment to the neurocranium. The removal of this is best done by making an incision in the skin overlaying the ventral surface of the neurocranium. Both gill-arches should remain attached to each other by a strip of tissue connecting them. The entire gill-arch can now be eased out and as much flesh as possible removed. Remove the gill filaments by cutting through at their dorsal ends and they will come away in one strip.

The eye can now be removed. This is quite straightforward. But before discarding, inspect to make sure that you have not removed the bony cups which are present in some species. A general clean-up can now be done by removing any remaining flesh, especially the lips from the mandible and premaxilla, and from the posterior medial surfaces of the mandible. The paired fins should also be dealt with at this stage.

It is now time to clean the axial skeleton and the median fins. The use of an improvised scraper can make short work of this task. Remember to leave intact the membranes that separate the right and left muscle masses of the interneural and interhaemal spines.

It may be difficult to clean the ribs, because their articulation is so nebulous.

Therefore leave an excess of tissue on their articulation at this stage. This excess can be removed more easily later.

Immediately after fleshing, the specimen should be soaked in a solution of 6 per cent ammonia and stored in a cool place for approximately twenty-four hours. The ammonia will toughen the ligaments, bleach the blood from the bones and cause any remaining bits of flesh to fluff up. On removing the specimen from the ammonia it is advisable to remove any large deposits of flesh before working the specimen with sodium hypochlorite.

It is important to note that there is a danger here, and the process should be carried out in a well-ventilated room, or better still in a fume cupboard. The mixture of sodium hypochlorite and ammonia can produce free chlorine gas. Take a plastic bristle brush, and brush the skeleton thoroughly with the solution. Rinse frequently, for if sodium hypochlorite is allowed to remain in the fins for any length of time damage may occur.

When washing has been completed, rinse thoroughly and allow to drain and dry. If degreasing is not considered necessary, bleaching can be carried out immediately. But if it is, the skeleton should be allowed to dry thoroughly and be degreased as already mentioned. Or it can be degreased by the recognised method for delicate bones – by trichlorethylene vapour.

The skeleton should be supported above the trichlorethylene solution so that the vapour can work. After this process, bleach the bones in 10 per cent hydrogen peroxide. Both degreasing and bleaching help to prevent the cartilage from yellowing. Bleaching should take between two and three hours.

Supporting for display

While the skeleton is still damp from the bleaching process a firm piece of brass, cut slightly longer than the specimen, is inserted into the external nares and pushed through the cranial cavity and through the neural arches as far as it will go. The excess wire which protrudes can be cut off so that no wire is visible.

The long job of arranging and pinning the skeleton can now begin. A mounting board is useful for this and can easily be made to suit the individual species. Pin the vertebral column and the median fins in position. The elements of the head, ribs and paired fins are now positioned and pins used to prop and secure them in place. When pinning and arranging is completed, put away in a warm dry place to dry. I find a sunny windowsill the ideal place. The sun will have an additional bleaching effect on the bones.

The specimen must be handled carefully when it is removed from its pinning surface. If any of the articulated points are weak, now is the time that they will come apart. A little glue or bone cement (made by dissolving table-tennis balls in acetone) will strengthen weak joints. The strip of skin which was left to outline the whole body can now be trimmed to an even narrower strip.

DEGREASING AGENTS

Carbon tetrachloride is a fine agent for the removal of grease from bones. Submerging the bones in a bath for a few days may be sufficient. Stubborn bones should be placed in a wire basket submerged in carbon tetrachloride. This can be heated up in a double boiler (used when melting animal glue) until it boils, which will be at about 75 °C (170 °F). The bones should then be boiled for a further fifteen minutes or so.

Remember that more carbon tetrachloride will be used in this way simply through evaporation. It is not a dangerous method, as carbon tetrachloride is a non-inflammable, or non-explosive, chemical. In fact for bones that are extra greasy, carbon tetrachloride can be mixed with benzine and the two ingredients boiled in the same way, the carbon tetrachloride rendering the benzine non-combustible. If the bones are subsequently to be bleached in peroxide, never use benzine alone as a degreasing agent. Peroxide is an aqueous solution and will not act on the greasy surface of a bone after it has been in benzine if you do not first remove this greasy deposit by submerging the bones in carbon tetrachloride.

To conclude the degreasing process,

remove the bones from the carbon tetra-chloride and place them in cold water containing a little ammonia, and heat until the grease rises to the surface. The bones are then placed into the bleaching agent. When sufficiently bleached, they are removed and laid on clean white paper to dry, if possible in the sun.

Other agents widely used for degreasing are acetone, benzine, xylene, chloroform and trichlorethylene. Take special care *not* to inhale the fumes. Always work either out of doors or in a fume cupboard which has a direct outward draught. The fumes of these chemicals are extremely dangerous so *take care*.

19
Preparing Habitats

A considerable knowledge of animals' behaviour and habitat is essential when preparing cases or larger dioramas. The larger museums throughout the world have on their staff highly skilled artists and trained model makers whose job it is to prepare and design the diorama, from the painting of the landscape to the modelling of the foliage and flowers. This method of preparing birds in their natural surroundings was first practised by E. T. Booth of Brighton in about 1860, who constructed a series of groups with artificially modelled habitats, showing the home lives of many British birds. These exhibits are still to be seen in the Booth Museum in Brighton. Mrs E. S. Mogridge and her brothers, Messrs Mintorn, introduced similar works into the Natural History Museum in South Kensington, London.

Works like these were interesting both to the general public and to the scientific fraternity. Every effort was made to render the habitats as scientifically accurate as possible, and after representatives from the American Museums saw these beautifully constructed exhibits, they invited Mrs Mogridge and her brothers to prepare a series for the New York Museum.

The art of making model foliage had a lot to do with the introduction of groups in museums, for the very crude milliner's leaves used in those early days were entirely inadequate. As the art of model-making advanced, taxidermy kept pace with it.

PRESERVING FOLIAGE

Much of the foliage used in habitats can be preserved and placed in the case or diorama after drying, such as mosses, lichens, sea-weed, ferns and many of the grasses. Leaves still attached to their particular piece of branch will also preserve successfully, such as elm, oak, birch, beech and also species that would be difficult to reproduce, like conifers and hemlock. Such foliage, however, does not have the same life as foliage made in wax, though they are at least botanically correct.

There are four basic ways of preserving plant material such as flowers, foliage, seed heads, leaves and grasses. These are air-drying, pressing, dessicant powder and glycerine.

The material to be preserved can be collected on a dry day, when there is a minimum amount of moisture on the plant surface. Never pick material when it is raining or when dew is forming. As a general rule, choose flowers just before they come to full bloom. Fully opened blossoms, or flowers that have already begun to set seed, will merely shed petals and seeds as you try to preserve them.

Air-drying

Pick the material and remove the leaves from the stems. Otherwise they will wither and die on the stems as they are drying. If the flowers are fairly small, put them into bunches and tie them with string, leaving a loop to slide on to a line or hook. If you have material with large flower heads, try to hang them separately. Otherwise they may be damaged when you try to disentangle the florets. As the material dries, it will tend to shrink, so you may find it necessary to tighten the string holding the stems.

The bunches should be hung well apart, on a line or on hooks in a cool, dry, airy and, if possible, dark place. Too much warmth and light tends to make the material brittle and faded. Flowers will become mildewed in damp surroundings. Flowers with heavy or fragile heads can be dried by standing them upright in a jar. For this method make sure that the plant has a strong stem and that the head does not droop. If the stems are very short, immediately after picking, cut them down to about one inch from the head and push a length of wire up the stem and into the flower head. The end of the wire can then be placed into a bed of sand or polystyrene block. Leave the flowers to dry in this position. The length of time needed for drying varies enormously. Delicate material such as grasses may only take a week. Heavier flowers, containing more moisture, may need three weeks or even more. The material must be checked to ensure that it is perfectly dry before removing for storage.

Pressing

Evergreens should be treated in a slightly different way. First, clean them by washing in luke-warm water to which a small amount of liquid detergent has been added. Rinse well, and shake gently to remove surplus moisture. Leave in an airy place to dry. When dry, place them between sheets of newspaper in layers one on top of the other, with a thick layer of paper between each layer. Tie all the layers into a parcel, making sure to protect the top and bottom with a sheet of cardboard. Place a light weight on top and leave for about a month, during which time the leaves will dry. This method stops the branches looking too flat, but if you want them flat, simply weigh down each single layer with a heavy weight. Ferns, which turn brown when they are dried, are best pressed flat in this way.

Desiccative powder

The powders used are borax, silica-gel crystals or sand. Of these silica-gel is probably the best and the most economical, as the crystals can be dried out in a warm oven after use and then used again. It dries flowers efficiently, and as the crystals are very light they are less likely to crush delicate blossoms.

One of the advantages of drying in powder is that the flowers preserved by this method retain much of their original colour. Before using a desiccative powder, you must ensure that the flowers are dry and in good condition. Cover the bottom of a container with the powder. Carefully lay the flowers on it, and pour over more of the powder until they are completely covered. Make sure that there is plenty of powder between the petals and the stamens, and take care not to add any moisture to the mixture by putting the box in a damp place. It must be kept in a warm dry place.

The drying time varies yet again. To test, gently scrape the powder from a petal. If any trace of moisture remains, recover and leave. Most small flowers take about two days to dry completely. Larger flowers will take six to seven days.

When the specimens are dry, remove and store them in a box, to which have been added a few crystals of silica-gel to absorb any moisture. Store in a dark place.

Florists' wire to support the stems must be added before drying.

Glycerine

This process replaces the water in the plant with glycerine, giving a supple and long-lasting result. The stems should be put in water for a few hours before placing them in the glycerine. Make sure that the material is in good condition: trying to preserve damaged leaves is a waste of effort. Woody stems should be split to ensure that the glycerine can travel along them. Make a mixture of two-parts boiling water to one-part glycerine, and when cool place the stems in about four inches of the liquid. Depending on the type of leaf being glycerined, the time necessary varies between two days and three weeks. The leaves should then become supple and change colour. Remove from the glycerine mixture, and if the leaves begin to droop, hang them upside down for a few days to ensure that the glycerine reaches the top. Material to be preserved by this method should be collected before the dying autumn colours begin to show. If you leave it too late, the plant loses its power to absorb liquid.

WIRING STEMS AND LEAVES

The stems of many of the everlasting flowers and of flowers that have been pre-served in a drying agent, although suitable for some habitat cases, may not be rigid enough for others. To overcome this problem, a false stem can be made by using florists' wire. It is essential to insert these wires before the flowers are dried. Pick the flower with about one inch of stem. If the stem is hollow or soft, push the wire through the stem and into the base of the flower, taking care not to penetrate through to the front of the flower itself. If the flower has a hard woody stem, the wire can be inserted into the base and laid along-side the natural stem. A short piece of wire will be sufficient at this stage, as it can be lengthened later. As the flower dries it shrinks and tightens around the wire, making a secure bond.

To lengthen a false or woody stem, simply place a piece of the required length of wire so that it overlaps the main stem by about one inch, and bind together with fine copper wire or similar. To lengthen a hollow stem, push the wire up through the stem and into the base of the flower. To give the false stem a more natural appear-ance, bind with gutta-percha tape.

For preserved leaves which need sup-port or a longer stem, use only a single piece of wire laid along the centre back of the leaf and hold in position with sellotape. If the leaf is large or broad, make a loop on the wire and place on the centre back of the leaf and secure with tape.

SKELETONISING LEAVES

It may be found necessary to add to habi-tats the skeletonised leaves which can be found in woodlands. A skeletonised leaf is one which has had all the soft green vege-table substance removed, either naturally or artificially, leaving a mass of exposed veins. The removal of the green substance occurs naturally when the leaf falls to the ground. Unfortunately leaves skeletonised in this way are often damaged and not suitable for use. One can achieve better results by using the following method:

Place a selected number of leaves in a metal container to which have been added a few ounces of washing soda. Simmer gently for one to two hours and allow to cool. By now the green substance should be soft enough to be removed by scraping gently with a knife or the fingers, under cold running water, great care being taken not to damage the veins. Test one leaf first. If not sufficiently softened, return the pan to the heat and simmer for a little longer. Finally, rinse the skeleton leaf thoroughly and dry between sheets of blotting paper or soft kitchen towel. At this stage the leaves are usually a dull shade of brown. If a paler colour is required, it can be pro-duced by leaving them in a solution of domestic bleach and water. Add one tablespoon of bleach to one pint of water and leave for twelve hours. Rinse and dry carefully. Most leaves with strong woody stems are suitable for this process.

DYEING GRASSES

Various methods are used to dye grasses, some of which can be very messy and totally unrewarding. The following methods take little trouble and produce very good results.

Although the grasses do not develop the bright gaudy hues that one would find in grasses bought from a florist, they do take on a more delicate, natural colour which blends in well with other foliage in the habitat.

Using 'food colouring', the basic solution is made with one tablespoon of dye to four ounces of water. The freshly cut grasses placed in this dye will absorb the solution and take on a soft shade of the colour being used, which will last indefinitely.

While some stems will readily take up the dye, others stubbornly remain green, even those taken from the same clump of grass. In this case, simply turn them upside down and submerge their heads in the dye and leave for several hours. Dry by the air-drying method.

Multi-purpose dyes

Mix the multi-purpose dye as instructed on the label, remembering that the amount of dye required will depend on the quantity of grasses to be dyed. The dye, when mixed, can be stored for a limited period in a screw-top container.

Using a suitable container, simmer the dye over a moderate heat. Then, holding the grasses by the stalks, immerse the heads in the dye, turning frequently to ensure that they are evenly dyed. Leave for about one minute, during which time the grasses will take on the colour. Dry on several sheets of newspaper. When dry, the broader leaves can be ironed with a warm iron to flatten them and leave them free of creases.

PLANT MODELLING

By far the best way of preparing botanical specimens is by reproducing the various parts of the plant in wax. The plant must, of course, be taken back to the workshop and dismantled, in order to make casts of its various parts.

Note that before removing plants from the wild, you must make sure the species is not in any way protected.

Photographs and drawings will aid in the reconstruction of the plant

Tools and materials

Pure white beeswax and paraffin wax M.P. 82 °C (180 °F) are required. A 50/50 mixture of the beeswax and paraffin wax will be found suitable for most purposes. For very fine work, such as delicate flowers and small leaves, use only beeswax. Fine dental plaster or colestone should be used for making the moulds. These are fine grained and hard setting.

Shellac dissoved in methylated spirits; or french polish, is used to coat the newly-made moulds. Plasticine or modelling clay is useful for making models from which moulds can be made. Fine silk or lawn, nylon thread and tinned copper wire for stems of various thicknesses.

Winsor and Newton oil colours, permanent shades. An assortment of brushes: fine, medium and large, hog hair and sable. Palette knives. A piece of plate glass measuring 36 in. × 12 in. × ¼ in. is also useful to work on from time to time.

Absorbent cotton-wool, blotting paper, tissue paper, crepe paper, glass wool. Powder colour for dusting, talcum powder, castor oil, linseed oil, glycerine, turpentine, Canada balsam or rosin and paraffin.

Fine-pointed scissors, curved and straight; small manicure scissors are useful for very fine work.

Metal and wooden modelling tools; Swan Morton scalpels with various shaped blades. Rectangular enamel dishes for producing sheets of wax. A double saucepan for melting large quantities of wax and an egg poacher for melting small quantities of different colours.

Making leaves

To make the leaf of the plant, an impression of the original leaf must be made. Smear the glass working surface with a thin coating of glycerine. Now place on this surface sufficient clay or plasticene to hold the leaf. Clay or plasticene is used so that the natural contours of the leaf can be followed. Walls are built around the object; these can be made of clay, plasticene, polystyrene or wood. Oil the upper surface of the leaf, and cover it with a creamy mixture of plaster. When dry, remove the mould from the table, leaving the leaf in the mould. Clean the edges of the leaf, and oil the underside of the leaf – and, of course, the edges of the mould itself. Place the mould on the working surface with the leaf uppermost, and build a similar set of walls as before. Pour on the plaster and allow it to set.

The two moulds can now be separated and the original leaf removed and discarded. When both moulds are thoroughly dry, they should be treated ready to receive the wax. This is done as follows:

Take half a pound of borax to two pints of water and mix thoroughly. Put this mixture and the moulds into a saucepan, put it on the stove and bring the solution to

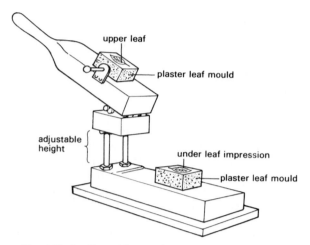

upper leaf

plaster leaf mould

adjustable height

under leaf impression

plaster leaf mould

Fig. 133. Leaf mould press for making wax leaves

the boil, allowing the moulds to simmer for about five minutes. This will harden them and prevent the fine edges of the mould from chipping, so lengthening the life of the mould. Remove the moulds from the borax water and store for future use. Before making the wax leaf from the moulds, submerge them in warm water for some fifteen minutes. Remove them and shake off the surplus water. Now place them into the squeeze-press ready to receive the wax.

To produce the wax leaf in this way you must work very quickly. First, impregnate the fine silk or crepe paper with wax by dipping it into the molten wax. Secondly, lay the impregnated fabric into the mould, position a supporting wire stem and then pour on some molten wax. Bring down the upper mould and apply pressure for a few seconds. The wax must not be allowed to cool when you first put it into the mould, or detail will be lost. It is imperative to have all the necessary equipment close at hand. The model leaf will easily lift from the damp mould.

The same procedure is carried out until you have the required number of leaves.

Simple leaf making

Take the chosen leaf and coat the top side of it with glycerine. Hot wax can now be painted on to its surface. In a few seconds the wax is hard and can be lifted off, giving

a true replica of the leaf. A supporting wire can be fused into the wax before removing it from the leaf. Leaves such as these are fine for filling in, but the back of the leaf carries no detail at all.

Making the stem

Probably the most important part of the model plant is the main stem. This must carry the whole weight of the finished plant, so that it stands in its correct position. Use a strong copper wire. This should extend from the apex of the plant to the root stock. The stem of the real plant is tapered towards the top, so our model must also taper. This is done by dipping the upper third into nitric acid, and drawing it out until the required tapering is reached.

Colour must be added to the hot wax. Artists' oil colour is used to achieve the correct shade of colour. Canada balsam or rosin should also be added to the wax, to give strength and hardness.

Three or more shades are mixed in containers in the steaming pan, so that when applying the wax to the main stem you can blend the colours together, beginning with pale green at the base of the stem and gradually getting deeper towards the top.

The wax is applied to the copper wire stem by painting it on with a hog's hair brush, the thickness being built up with successive coats of wax until the correct taper and appearance is obtained.

The now waxed wire can be rolled on to the plate-glass working surface to work out any imperfections. Wax can also be sand-papered with very fine sandpaper, or wiped with cotton-wool soaked in turpentine or paraffin to remove minor blemishes. Preparing plants such as square-stemmed St John's wort *(Hypericum tetrapterum)* which, as its name suggests, has square stems, is done by forming the wax with a modelling tool or dull scalpel. The grooves are added later by holding the now square stem between the thumb and forefinger of one hand and drawing the stem upwards with the other. The groove is cut with a thumbnail or the edge of the modelling tool. This process is continued all round the stem until the required number of grooves have been cut.

Making the flowers

Fine silk sheets are cut to a workable size (6 in. × 3 in.). This size obviously depends on the size of the petal to be reproduced.

The silk sheets are now dipped into molten wax and withdrawn carefully, allowing the surplus wax to drain off. The sheets are laid on one side. The flower to be modelled is dissected, and patterns of each petal are made. The pattern can be made by laying the petal on the wax and marking round it. These are cut out carefully from the waxed silk and shaped in the palm of the hand with the aid of a wooden modelling tool. The warmth from the hand will soon make the little wax petal flexible and

made, place on one side until the completed number is ready. A single bead, as used in ladies' jewellery, is secured to the end of each stem, and then it is dipped into hot wax. This forms the core of the flower. Waxed threads are fused to the base of this core to form the stamens, and the end of each stamen is touched with a globule of wax to form the anthers. Buds are formed in a similar way, using beads of various sizes. The sepals are modelled as described for the petals and fixed into place round the waxed bead.

Assembling the plant

When the leaves, flowers and buds have been modelled and completed, they are ready to be assembled. Beginning at the top of the stem, the flowers and the buds are rolled together at their bases, tied and fused to the main stem. Continuing down the stem, each leaf is tied and fused in position, following the shape of the plant species being modelled. If the plant is to be put into a diorama, no roots will be necessary. But if the plant is to be displayed as a botanical specimen they must be made. Roots are made from wax-covered wires and the rootlets from waxed cotton threads.

To complete the model, hand paint and tint it where necessary. As soon as the specimen is dry, it can be placed into its desired display position.

Bibliography

Anderson, R. M., *Methods of Collecting and Preserving Vertebrate Animals*, Bulletin No. 69, Biological Series No. 18, National Museum of Canada 1965

Baldwin, S. P., Oberholser, H. C. and Worley, L. G., *Measurements of Birds*, vol. 2, Cleveland Museum of Natural History 1931

Beddard, Frank E., *The Structure and Classification of Birds*, London 1889

Browne, Montagu, *Practical Taxidermy*, London 1884

Corbet, G. B., *The Identification of British Mammals*, British Museum Natural History, London 1969

Cornwallis & Smith, *The Bird in the Hand*, London 1960

Davie, Oliver, *Methods in the Art of Taxidermy*, Philadelphia 1900

Ellenberger, W., Dittrich, H. and Baun, H., *An Atlas of Animal Anatomy for Artists*, ed. Louis F. Brown, New York 1956

Harris, R. H., 'Vacuum Dehydration and Freeze-Drying of Entire Biological Specimens', *Natural History* series 13, vol. 7, 65–74, 1964

Harrison, J. M., *Bird Taxidermy*, Shooting Times Library No.18, London 1964

Hornaday, *Taxidermy and Zoological Collecting*, New York 1891

Hower, Rolland O., *Freeze-drying Biological Specimens* (a laboratory manual), Washington D.C. 1980

Irvin, A. D., Cooper, J. E. and Hedges, S. R., 'Possible Health Hazards Associated with the Collection and Handling of Postmortem Zoological Material', *Mammal Review*, vol. 2, no. 2, London 1972

Irvin, A. D., *The Epidemiology of Wildlife Rabies*, Surrey 1970

Manesse, Abbé, *Treatise on the Manner of Stuffing and Preserving Animals and Skins*, Paris 1786

Maynard, C. J., *Manual of Taxidermy* (a complete guide in collecting and preserving birds and mammals), Boston 1884

Moyer, John W., *Practical Taxidermy, a Working Guide*, New York 1953

Roche, Jean, 'The Preparation of Osteological Specimens', original paper on the Perborate Method, *Extrait de Mammalia*, tome XVIII, No. 4

Rowley, John, *Taxidermy and Museum Exhibition*, London & New York 1925

Shilling, Dr W., *The Manner of Collecting and Preparing Fishes and Reptiles*, Weimar 1860–61

Southeran, H. N., *A Handbook of British Mammals*, Oxford 1964

Stollas, M. B., *Instructions on the Manner of Preparing Objects of Natural History*, Paris 1752

Svensson, L., *Identification Guide to European Passerines*, Natürhistoriske Riksmuseet, Sweden 1970

Twigg, G. I., 'Rat-borne Leptospirosis in Wildlife and on the Farm', *Mammal Review* 3 (2), London 1973

Wagstaffe, R. and Fidler H. J., *The Preservation of Natural History Specimens*, vol. 2, Welwyn Garden City 1968

Ward, Rowland, *A Naturalist's Life Study in the Art of Taxidermy*, London 1913

Williamson, K., *Identification for Ringers*, vols. 1–3, British Trust for Ornithology 1960–64

Witherby, H. F., Jourdain, F., Ticehurst, N. and Tucker, B., *The Handbook of British Birds*, London 1940

Appendix 1

Taxidermists and the Law

Taxidermists must be in no doubt about the protection of birds and other animals throughout the world. They must make themselves aware of the protection laws governing whatever country they are working in. In some cases offences are committed in ignorance of the law, and it is for this reason that I have attempted to give the main parts of the British Protection of Birds Acts 1954, 1967 and 1976, and the Conservation of Wild Creatures and Wild Plants Act 1975.

The protection of our wild birds is very important; in my opinion the law is not strict enough with proved offenders. Copies of these British Protection Acts can be obtained from Her Majesty's Stationery Office, 49 High Holborn, London WC1. It is important to remember that legislation is constantly changing; consequently the law will change as species are transferred from schedule to schedule. You should keep up to date with these changes. Booklets listing the schedules for protected birds can be obtained from the Royal Society for the Protection of Birds, The Lodge, Sandy, Bedfordshire SG19 2DL.

Taxidermists practising in the USA can obtain copies of the relevant laws concerning all wildlife from the Law Enforcement Office, Fish and Wildlife Service, US Department of the Interior, C Street between 18th and 19th Street North West, Washington DC 20240, USA.

PROTECTION OF BIRDS ACTS

The British Protection of Birds Acts 1954, 1967, 1976, and in particular sections 1 and 6 (1) (d) of the 1954 Act, are paraphrased below; for the precise wording reference should be made to the Act itself. In Britain, the Act forms the basis of the British bird protection laws; it is therefore vital that those practising taxidermy should familiarise themselves with its provisions. Its premise is that all wild birds and their nests and eggs must be protected at all times from deliberate molestation.

It states categorically that it is an offence to have possession of, or control of, a wild bird which has been recently killed or taken. Special penalties come into force if these offences are committed against our rarer birds, i.e. those just beginning to establish themselves as British breeding birds, or those which are rare throughout their range, thus needing all the protection we can give them.

Section 1

This gives general prohibitions against the taking of wild birds, their nests and eggs and penalises:

(a) any person who wilfully kills, injures or takes or even attempts to kill, injure or take any wild bird;

(b) any person who takes, damages or destroys the nest while that nest is in use; and

(c) any person who removes the eggs or destroys them.

If anyone has in their possession a recently killed or taken bird, which is not shown to have been taken legally, once again they are liable to prosecution.

Section 2

This section lists a number of instances where the general protection created by section 1 is qualified.

1. The birds listed in schedule 2 may be killed or taken by the lawful occupiers of land and certain other 'authorised persons' (an owner of land, or a person with permission to use land) on weekdays throughout the year in England, Wales and Scotland. Schedule 2 birds, however, are fully protected on Sundays and Christmas Day in Scotland and on Sundays in certain 'prescribed areas'.

2. Authorised persons may destroy the nests and take the eggs of schedule 2 birds, and may

also take the eggs of wild duck, geese and swans, where this is done with a view to using them for hatching purposes. Also, any person may destroy the eggs of schedule 2 birds and may take (but only for certain purposes) the eggs of Black-headed Gull and Common Gull and may destroy or take the eggs of Lapwing before 15 April in any year. None of these activities is lawful on Christmas Day or Sundays in Scotland.

Section 3

The birds that are mentioned in schedule 3 are fully protected together with their nests and eggs only during the close season, as defined in subsection 2; otherwise they are protected only on Sundays and Christmas Day in Scotland and on Sundays in certain parts of England and Wales.

The following sections are the most important for the would-be taxidermist. They should be read with the greatest care.

RECENTLY KILLED AND TAKEN BIRDS

Section 6

This section puts the burden of proving his innocence on any person who can be shown by the prosecution to have had in his possession any wild bird which has been recently taken. This covers a great number of commercial, sporting and other activities, so I include only those provisions relevant to the taxidermist.

Restrictions are placed upon sale of live or dead wild birds or eggs:

1. If, save as may be authorised by a licence granted under section 10 of this Act, any person sells, offers for sale or has in his possession for sale:

(a) any live wild bird, being a bird that is of the species which is resident in or visits the British Isles in the wild state, other than an aviary-bred bird which has been close-ringed.

(b) an egg (including a blown egg) of a wild bird of any species, which is known to nest in the wild state in the British Isles.

(c) a dead wild goose taken during the close season, which is from 28 February to 31 August, or any other dead bird that is protected under schedule 3 or any wild duck whether that species is included in the schedule or not.

(d) a dead wild bird other than such a bird

that is mentioned in paragraph (c) unless it was known that the bird was taken legally, as per museum procedure, i.e. sent in by a donor, road accident, or was lawfully imported.

(e) the skin of a wild bird other than such a bird as is mentioned in paragraph (c) unless it is shown that the skin or plumage came from a bird which was killed legally, i.e. road accident, or that the skin or plumage was lawfully imported. Then one should be guilty of an offence against this act. However, if the offence was committed in respect of a bird which is included in the first schedule of the act or in respect of an egg, skin or plumage of such a bird then one shall be liable to a special penalty.

2. If a Justice of the Peace is satisfied by information on oath that there is reasonable ground to suspect that an offence has been committed under this section and that the evidence may be found on any premises, he may grant a warrant to any constable to enter and search those premises for the purpose of obtaining that evidence.

Wild creatures have to endure so many human pressures, that there is no excuse for taking wild birds illegally. Recent court cases in Great Britain, brought by the Royal Society for the Protection of Birds, show that taxidermists are liable to be convicted under the Act. If they have in their possession or control birds that have been unlawfully killed. Equally, they are liable to conviction if they are in possession of dead birds for sale, if those birds have been taken or imported unlawfully.

Taxidermists might follow the example of some museums and notify their donors or customers that 'any protected bird killed, taken or imported illegally' that is brought to their attention must be reported to the Police, R.S.P.C.A. or R.S.P.B.

RESTRICTIONS ON IMPORTATION OF CERTAIN WILD BIRDS AND EGGS

Section 7

1. Unless authorised by a licence granted under section 10 of the act, the importation of any of the following is strictly prohibited:

(a) any common quail whether alive or dead;
(b) from 1 February to 31 August any dead bird which is included in schedule 3 of

this act or any wild duck or wild goose, whether that species is included or not; and

(c) any dead Lapwing or its eggs.

BIRDS OF PREY

It is an offence to import live hawks of the Falconiformes, of which there are 271 species, and also live owls of the order Strigiformes, of which there are 134 species, unless one has been granted a licence under section 10. This prohibition lasts throughout the year. These papers can be obtained by writing to Her Majesty's Stationery Office and quoting S.I. 1970 No. 545.

PROTECTION OF CAPTIVE BIRDS

Section 8

1. If any person keeps or confines any wild bird whatsoever, in any cage or other receptacle which is not sufficient in height, length or breadth to permit the bird to stretch its wings freely, he shall be guilty of an offence and be liable to a special penalty unless,

(a) that bird is in the course of being transported by land, air or water.
(c) the bird is being shown for the purpose of any public exhibition or competition, if the time during which the bird is confined does not in the aggregate exceed seventy-two hours.

The above also applies to birds undergoing treatment by veterinary surgeons or veterinary practitioners.

2. Every person who promotes, arranges, conducts, assists in, receives money for, or takes part in, any event whatsoever in the course of which captive birds are liberated by hand or by any other means for the purpose of being shot immediately after their release, or who, being the owner or occupier of any land, permits that land to be used for the purposes of such an event, shall be guilty, prosecuted and be liable to a special penalty.

LICENCES GRANTING EXEMPTION FROM THE ACT

Section 10

1. A licence may be granted to any person by the appropriate authority specified in the following subsection. However, it is subject to compliance with any conditions specified in the licence.

(a) for scientific or educational purposes, enabling one to kill or take within any specified area (noted on the licence) or to sell or import alive or dead, any number of wild birds specified, it also includes their nests and eggs, including blown eggs.
(b) for the purpose of falconry, to take by any means any raptor specified in the licence or to sell or import alive any number of birds; the species is of course specified.
(c) for the purpose of the protection of any collection of birds, maintained at any place and by any person. This enables one to kill or take at the place specified, by any means mentioned in the licence wild birds of any description.
(d) for the purposes of killing or taking such wild birds included in schedule 2 as may be specified in the licence, to use any poisoned poisonous or stupefying substance of any description specified.
(e) for the purpose of taking wild birds in order to ring or mark, or examine any ring or mark, all or any of the birds taken must then be released, to use within any area specified in the licence, any form of artificial light or any net for taking birds in flight and the use of any rocket-propelled or cannon nets for taking birds on the ground.

2. The appropriate authority for the grant of a licence under the foregoing subsection shall be:

in the case of a licence under paragraph (a), (b), or (e) of that subsection, the Secretary of State after consultation with the appropriate advisory committee.
in the case of a licence under paragraph (a) or (e) of that subsection which is required for the purposes of scientific or educational work carried out by, or on behalf of, or with the aid of grants from, the Nature Conservancy Council.
in the case of a licence under paragraph (c) of that subsection, the Secretary of State.
in the case of a licence under paragraph (d) of that subsection, the Minister of Agriculture, Fisheries and Food or, in Scotland, the Secretary of State.

3. A licence granted under this section may be revoked at any time by the authority by whom it was granted; and, without prejudice to any other liability to a penalty which he may have incurred under this or any other Act, any person who contravenes or fails to comply with any condition imposed on the grant of a licence under this section shall be guilty of an offence against this Act.

These licences generally contain conditions. There is no immunity from prosecution where acts are done in breach of such conditions.

CONSERVATION OF WILD CREATURES AND WILD PLANTS ACT 1975

The purpose of this Act is to prevent people from killing, capturing or maiming wild creatures, and from uprooting and destroying wild plants.

Wild creatures

It is an offence to kill, injure or take, or attempt to kill, injure or take, any protected wild creatures. It is an offence to have in your possession any protected wild creature unless it can be proved that it was not taken or killed in contravention of this Act. The offender may not be charged under this Act if he is able to prove that his action in killing such a protected wild creature was for the prevention of damage to his land and property.

If any person is found selling either dead or alive protected wild creatures listed in schedule 1 (see p. 144), he shall be found guilty unless he is able to offer a reasonable excuse for his action. It is important to note that this also includes the sale of skins and skeletons of dead protected wild creatures.

It is an offence to mark or ring any protected wild creatures.

Wild plants

Any unauthorised person who, without reasonable excuse, uproots any plants, is guilty of an offence. It is an offence to pick, uproot or destroy any protected plant (see pp. 144-5).

General exceptions

There are exceptions to being charged under this Act. If you have taken a disabled protected wild creature for the purpose of caring for it, or if you have killed, or attempted to kill, a seriously injured wild creature as an act of mercy, you are not guilty of an offence.

Power to grant licences

A licence may be applied for and granted to authorise certain people to collect wild creatures and wild plants for conservation, scientific or educational purposes, in certain specified areas only. This licence can also be granted to certain authorities in order to prevent the spreading of disease.

If an authorised person suspects that someone on his land is committing, or has committed, an offence against the Act, he can order him off his land and report him to the authorities.

THE NATURE CONSERVANCY COUNCIL ACT 1973

The Act grants the right to this council to review the Schedules to this Act at any time, and wild creatures and wild plants may be added, particularly if the wild creature or plant has become so rare that its survival is being endangered. Or it might be that some species have re-established themselves and are no longer at risk; these then can be removed from the Schedules.

It is most important to be aware of the protected wild creatures and wild plants. Few people know how much of our wild life is protected by law, and there is a fine of £100 for any offence.

PROTECTED BIRDS

Schedule 1: Part I

Wild birds and their eggs protected by special penalties *at all times*.

Avocet
Bee-eater (all species)
Bittern (all species)
Bluethroat
Brambling
Bunting, snow
Buzzard, honey
Chough
Corncrake
Crake, spotted
Crossbill
Diver (all species)
Dotterel
Eagle (all species)
Falcon, Gyr
Fieldfare
Firecrest
Godwit, black-tailed

Goshawk
Grebe, black-necked
Grebe, Slavonian
Greenshank
Gull, little
Gull, Mediterranean
Harrier (all species)
Heron, purple
Hobby
Hoopoe
Kingfisher
Kite
Merlin
Oriole, golden
Osprey
Owl, barn
Owl, snowy
Peregrine
Phalarope, red-necked
Plover, Kentish
Plover, little ringed
Quail, European
Redstart, black
Redwing
Rosefinch, scarlet
Ruff and reeve
Sandpiper, green
Sandpiper, wood
Serin
Shorelark
Shrike, red-backed
Sparrowhawk
Spoonbill
Stilt, black-winged
Stint, Temminck's
Stone curlew
Swan, whooper
Tern, black
Tern, little
Tern, roseate
Tit, bearded
Tit, crested
Treecreeper, short-toed
Warbler, Cetti's
Warbler, Dartford
Warbler, marsh
Warbler, Savi's
Woodlark
Wryneck

Schedule 1: Part II

Wild birds and their eggs protected by special penalties *during the close season* 1 February to 31 August but which may be killed or taken at other times.

Whimbrel
Wild duck of the following species have the same close season except that in or over any area

below high water mark the close season runs from 21 February to 31 August.
Common scoter
Garganey
Goldeneye
Long-tailed duck
Pintail
Scaup
Velvet scoter

Schedule 2

Wild birds which may be killed or taken by authorised persons.

Bullfinch (only in certain areas)
Cormorant
Crow, carrion
Crow, hooded
Domestic pigeon (gone feral)
Dove, collared
Goosander (Scotland only)
Gull, great black-backed
Gull, lesser black-backed
Gull, herring
Jackdaw
Jay
Magpie
Merganser, red-breasted (Scotland only)
Oystercatcher (only in certain areas)
Raven (Argyll and Skye only)
Rock dove (Scotland only)
Rook
Shag
Sparrow, house
Starling
Stock dove
Woodpigeon

Schedule 3

Wild birds which may be killed or taken *outside the close season*, 1 February to 31 August except where indicated otherwise. Note that the close season for wild duck and geese when below high water mark is 21 February to 31 August.

Those birds already shown in Part II of Schedule 1.
Capercaillie – close season 1 February to 30 September
Coot
Curlew (other than stone curlew)
Gannet (on Sula Sgeir only)
Godwit, bar-tailed
Snipe, common – close season 1 February to 11 August
Snipe, jack – close season 1 February to 11 August

Taxidermy

Wild duck of the following species (see note above)
Common pochard
Gadwall
Mallard
Shoveler
Teal
Tufted duck
Wigeon

Wild geese of the following species (see note above)
Bean goose
Canada goose
Greylag goose
Pink-footed goose
White-footed goose

Woodcock – close season 1 February to 30 September except in Scotland, where it is 1 February to 31 August.

Schedule 4

Wild birds which may *not* be sold alive unless close-ringed and bred in captivity:

Blackbird
Blackcap
Bluethroat
Brambling
Bullfinch
Bunting (all species)
Chaffinch
Chiffchaff
Chough
Crossbill (all species)
Cuckoo
Dipper
Fieldfare
Firecrest
Flycatcher (all species)
Goldcrest
Goldfinch
Greenfinch
Hawfinch
Hoopoe
Jay
Kingfisher
Lark (all species)
Linnet
Magpie
Martin (all species)
Nightingale
Nightjar
Nuthatch
Oriole, golden
Owl (all species except the little owl)
Pipit (all species)
Raven

Redpoll (all species)
Redstart (all species)
Redwing
Ring ouzel
Robin
Shrike (all species)
Siskin
Sparrow, hedge
Sparrow, house
Sparrow, tree
Starling
Stonechat
Swallow
Thrush (all species)
Tit (all species including bearded tit)
Treecreeper
Twite
Wagtail (all species)
Warbler (all species)
Waxwing
Wheatear
Whinchat
Whitethroat (all species)
Woodpecker (all species)
Wren
Wryneck
Yellowhammer

PROTECTED WILD CREATURES

Schedule 1

Greater horse-shoe bat
  Rhinolophus ferrumequinum
Mouse-eared bat
  Myotis myotis
Sand lizard
  Lacerta agilis
Smooth snake
  Coronella austriaca
Natterjack toad
  Bufo calamita
Large blue butterfly
  Maculinea arion
Common otter
  Lutra lutra

PROTECTED PLANTS

Schedule 2

Alpine gentian
  Gentiana nivalis
Alpine sow-thistle
  Cicerbita alpina
Alpine woodsia
  Woodsia alpina

Blue heath
  Phyllodoce caerulea
Cheddar pink
  Dianthus gratianopolitanus
Diapensia
  Diapensia lapponica
Drooping saxifrage
  Saxifraga cernua
Ghost orchid
  Epipogium aphyllum
Killarney fern
  Trichomanes speciosum
Lady's slipper
  Cypripedium calceolus
Mezereon
  Daphne mezereum
Military orchid
  Orchis militaris

Monkey orchid
  Orchis simia
Oblong woodsia
  Woodsia ilvensis
Red helleborine
  Cephalanthera rubra
Snowdon lily
  Lloydia serotina
Spiked speedwell
  Veronica spicata
Spring gentian
  Gentiana verna
Teesdale sandwort
  Minuartia stricta
Tufted saxifrage
  Saxifraga cespitosa
Wild gladiolus
  Gladiolus illyricus

Appendix 2

Check-list of Diseases Contagious to Man

This list first appeared in *Mammal Review* (1972) 2, No. 2.

BACTERIAL DISEASES

Anthrax

Species involved – *Artiodactyla* and others.

Symptoms in animals – sudden death and haemorrhage from orifices; enlarged spleen; blood fails to clot. Some species (e.g. *Suidae*) are less susceptible to infection and may recover.

Sources of agent – spores on hides; bone dust; blood of infected animals.

Route of infection – oral; respiratory; skin lesion.

Resistance – spores formed under aerobic conditions are very resistant to chemical and physical agents. In carcasses vegetative forms die in one to two weeks. Strong hypochlorite and warm formaldehyde vapour are most effective in destroying spores.

Symptoms in man – cutaneous form – malignant pustule. Respiratory form 'Wool Sorter's Disease' (pneumonia and septicaemia); often fatal.

Brucellosis

Species involved – *Bovidae*, especially cattle and goats; also hares and pigs.

Symptoms in animals – abortion; foetal membranes become leathery; orchitis in males; joint lesions.

Sources of agent – genital system and products of abortion.

Route of infection – oral; cutaneous; conjuctiva.

Resistance – when protected by host material, may be several months. Survives well at low temperatures. Sensitive to sunlight; phenol; formalin and quaternary ammonium compounds.

Symptoms in man – ascending lymphadenitis; indulent fever; orchitis; persistent infection.

Erysipelas (Erysipelothrix rhusiopathiae)

Species involved – *Suidae;* marine mammals; occasionally birds.

Symptoms in animals – skin rash and fever in pigs; usually commensal organism in marine mammals.

Sources of agent – infected secretions and blood; cutaneous slime of marine mammals.

Route of infection – puncture wound; oral.

Resistance – readily destroyed by desiccation and common disinfecting agents.

Symptoms in man – Erysipeloid – local skin lesion; swelling; redness; irritation and local lymphadenitis, 'Blubber Finger'.

Leptospirosis

Species involved – rodents, especially *Muridae;* also hedgehogs, hares and probably a wide range of other mammals.

Symptoms in animals – usually symptomless; may be kidney lesions and sometimes jaundice.

Sources of agent – urine or urinary system; or contaminated material.

Route of infection – wound or skin penetration; conjuctiva.

Resistance – die rapidly outside the body and in dry environment; sensitive to common disinfecting agents.

Symptoms in man – fever; influenza-like symptoms; muscle pains; may be severe conditions (Weils' Disease); jaundice.

Plague (Pasteurella pestis)

Species involved – bubonic form – rats and mice; sylvatic form – gerbils; ground squirrels and other burrowing rodents.

Symptoms in animals – caseous and necrotic lesions, especially in axillary and inguinal lymph nodes (bubo). Generalised symptoms, often death.

Sources of agent – fleas are vectors of the disease; flea faeces and contaminated dust.

Route of infection – flea bite; infected faeces or dust inhaled or rubbed into skin lesions.

Resistance – survives on skins – few days; in dried flea faeces – five weeks; refridgerated – several years. Killed by sunlight in three to four hours. Destroyed by common agents.

Symptoms in man – inflammation and pain at infected site; swollen lymph nodes and bubo formation. Generalised – sudden onset; fever; collapse; central nervous system upset; often fatal.

Special precautions – destroy fleas e.g. by fumigation; avoid contact with flea faeces – use gloves; destroy infected material.

Pseudotuberculosis (Pasteurella pseudotuberculosis)

Species affected – most birds, sometimes rodents and other small mammals.

Symptoms in animals – necrotic nodules in all organs especially spleen and liver; emaciation.

Sources of agent – faeces of infected animal or carcass if opened.

Route of infection – oral; inhalation; puncture wound.

Resistance – survives few days if dry. Destroyed by usual disinfectants.

Symptoms in man – rare condition; abdominal pain, may simulate appendicitis. Commoner in young people.

Psittacosis

Caused not by true bacteria but by organisms of the genus Chlamydia.

Species affected – primarily *Psittacidae*, but very contagious and may easily be spread to birds of other families.

Symptoms in birds – diarrhoea; nasal discharge; frequently fatal. Also symptomless carriers; enlarged spleen seen at postmortem.

Sources of agent – faeces; carcass; contaminated feathers.

Route of infection – inhalation; occasionally oral.

Resistance – survives few hours if dry, weeks if frozen. Destroyed by usual disinfectants.

Symptoms in man – rapid onset; fever; pneumonia; may be fatal if untreated.

Special precautions – dampen feathers of all psittacines with disinfectant before handling.

Ornithosis

Describes psittacosis as seen in non-psittacine birds

Species involved – very widespread; over twenty-seven families recorded.

Symptoms in birds – usually none, may appear as mild psittacosis.

Sources of agent – as psittacosis.

Route of infection – as psittacosis

Resistance – as psittacosis

Symptoms in man – usually mild but may be severe, rather persistent influenza-like symptoms. Persistent running nose and eyes with occasional bout of fever.

Special precautions – as psittacosis

Salmonellosis

Species affected – all species, but types most dangerous to man more likely from rodents; hedgehogs; captive primates; reptiles and from peri-domestic birds – e.g. pigeons, gulls.

Symptoms in animals – may be enteritis and fever, but some may be symptomless carriers.

Sources of agent – gastro-intestinal tract and contaminated material.

Route of infection – oral; occasionally other routes.

Resistance – can survive weeks, possibly months, especially if protected in dry faeces. Formalin best common disinfectant.

Symptoms in man – fever; abdominal pain; diarrhoea.

147

Shigellosis

Species involved – primates.

Symptoms in animals – very variable from mild to acute. Gastroenteritis; diarrhoea; fever; may be symptomless.

Sources of agent – gastro–intestinal tract and contaminated material.

Route of infection – oral.

Resistance – survives few days unprotected, but may last months if protected by organic material. Easily destroyed by common disinfecting agents if not protected.

Symptoms in man – gastro–enteritis; fever; abdominal pain; diarrhoea; rash.

Tetanus

Species involved – principally *Artiodactyla* but any species can pick up infection from the soil.

Symptoms in animals – bacterial toxin is the cause of symptoms, muscle spasms; paralysis.

Sources of agent – bacterial spores are found in the soil, dust, animal faeces.

Route of infection – puncture or deep wounds where anaerobic multiplication of the organism can occur with toxin release.

Resistance – spores are highly resistant; vegetative forms killed by usual disinfectants.

Symptoms in man – muscle spasm and paralysis (lockjaw). Often fatal.

Special precautions – prophylactic anti-tetanus injections; following puncture and deep wounds, a doctor should be consulted and anti-toxin may be administered.

Tuberculosis (Avian)

Species affected – all species.

Symptoms in birds – emaciation; yellow or white foci on liver, intestine.

Sources of agent – faeces of infected bird or organs if carcass opened.

Route of infection – oral; inhalation; puncture wound.

Resistance – survives months, possibly years on infected material. Destroyed by prolonged exposure to phenol, formalin.

Symptoms in man – rather resistant to infection. Malaise; loss of weight; local inflammation and ascending lymphadenitis following puncture wound.

Special precautions – expose liver of all carcasses; if found infected disinfect well and destroy carcass.

Tuberculosis (Mammalian)

Species involved – cattle; deer; animals in contact with man (especially primates) or domestic animals (especially *Artiodactyla*). Relatively uncommon in free-living wild animals.

Symptoms in animals – emaciation; chronic cough; lymphadenitis symptoms vary according to site of infection.

Sources of agent – tuberculous lesions especially lungs and lymph nodes; organisms may therefore be shed in sputum; faeces; bone lesions.

Route of infection – inhalation; oral; puncture wound.

Resistance – survives in dried state in dark for two to twelve weeks. Rather resistant to chemical agents. Sensitive to ultra-violet light.

Symptoms in man – depends on route of infection – pneumonia; chronic cough; lymphadenitis; wasting.

Special precautions – regular attendance at mass X-ray centres. Prophylactic BCG vaccination.

Tularaemia

Species involved – burrowing rodents; lemmings; ground squirrels; lagomorpha.

Symptoms in animals – caseous and necrotic lesions in axillary and inguinal lymph nodes; liver; spleen.

Sources of agent – blood, urine, saliva of infected animals. Ticks fed on infected animals

Route of infection – highly contagious. Skin; conjunctiva; mucous membranes; tick bites.

Resistance – survives in skin – forty days; carcasses – four months. Refrigeration will prolong survival time. Inactivated by common agents, e.g. 0.1 per cent formalin.

Symptoms in man – skin rash and ulceration; ascending lymphadenitis; fever; conjunctivitis; pneumonia.

VIRAL DISEASES

B Virus (Herpesvirus simiae)

Species involved – monkeys and macaques, but all primates are probably a risk, especially Old World species. Related viruses are not uncommon in New World species, e.g. squirrel monkeys.

Symptoms in animals – ulcers on tongue and lips similar to cold sores in man. Mild condition in natural hosts.

Sources of agent – salivary system; also blood.

Route of infection – skin wounds; monkey bites.

Resistance – short-lived in dry state; may persist many months in frozen carcasses. Destroyed by desiccation and common disinfectants.

Symptons in man – local inflammation at site of infection followed by encephalitis, usually fatal.

Special precautions – protect hands and arms; thoroughly wash and clean any abrasions incurred while handling fresh or frozen primate material, and report to a medical officer. Destroy suspect material.

Rabies

Species involved – Carnivora and neotropical bats, especially *Desmodus* spp. However, all mammals are susceptible to infection.

Symptoms in animals – in most animals; mania; paralysis and death in convulsions. Vampire bats and a few other species can be symptomless carriers.

Sources of agent – salivary system, central nervous system; brown fat of bats.

Route of infection – skin wounds or bites; inhalation very rarely.

Resistance – in dried saliva, fourteen hours. In frozen material, several months. At room temperature, several weeks; Freeze-dried, years. Immersion of brains and skulls in 4 per cent formalin or 70 per cent alcohol for several weeks will inactivate the virus. Destroyed by repeated freezing and thawing.

Symptoms in man – long incubation period, often several months; uneasiness; depression leading to progressive paralysis; convulsion; invariably fatal once symptoms commence.

Special precautions – prophylactic vaccination.

Vervet monkey disease (Marburg agent)

Species involved – vervet monkey; other species susceptible to experimental infection. Very much an unknown quantity but probably rare condition.

Symptoms in animals – experimental infection in monkeys – symptoms as in man, but 100 per cent fatal.

Sources of agent – blood; urine; saliva.

Route of infection – aerosol route and through intact skin.

Resistance – survives at room temperature for more than five weeks. Sensitive to common disinfectants.

Symptoms in man – fever; rash on face and trunk; lymphadenitis; abdominal upsets. 30–40 per cent mortality.

FUNGAL DISEASES

The majority of fungi invading man or animals (excluding the ringworm fungi - considered separately) are normally found as saprophytes on decomposing organic material (e.g. *Sporotrichum, Aspergillus*) or in the soil (e.g. *Histoplasma, Coccidioides*). Under certain conditions the fungi can establish themselves as 'parasites'. In man they tend to be 'opportunistic invaders' attacking when the body's resistance is lowered, e.g. *Histoplasma* and *Aspergillus* may attack the lungs following respiratory complaints.

Man and animals are usually infected when exposed to a heavily contaminated environment; transmission of fungi by infected animals to other animals (including man) is rare.

Fungal infections of small mammals, including bats, are not uncommon in certain localised areas, but these infections are probably indicative of a contaminated environment rather than endemic infection. This contamination may persist in mud or soil on animal hides and packing materials.

The risk of contracting such fungal infections from handling skins or carcasses is probably small, but because they form spores, fungi are rather resistant to chemical and physical agents and some, e.g. *Coccidioides,* may persist for several months on skins. Risks can be minimised by the use of gloves and face masks, and by ensuring adequate ventilation, particularly when opening newly arrived material. Soaking specimens in 2 per cent formalin, or damping down with Cetrimide solution before examination are also recommended.

Aspergillosis

Species involved – all birds, but especially aquatic and gallinaceous birds which can acquire infection from decaying vegetable matter. Mammals occasionally affected.

Symptoms in animals – variable; often pneumonic symptoms; also skin lesions; poor condition. Fungus apparent if carcass opened. May be abortion in mammals.

Sources of agent – little danger unless dead animal opened to expose fungus in body cavity. Skin lesions.

Route of infection – inhalation.

Resistance – vegetative form of fungus sensitive to desiccation but spores may survive months. Normal disinfectants will destroy, but need considerable time.

Symptoms in man – pneumonia

Histoplasmosis

Species involved – cave dwelling and small burrowing mammals and bats.

Symptoms in animals – encapsulated lung lesions; occasionally generalised.

Sources of agent – usually from dust etc., on animals' skins contaminated from their environment. Packing materials.

Route of infection – respiratory.

Resistance – spores are very resistant to physical agents. Quaternary ammonium compounds are most effective in destroying.

Symptoms in man – usually mild or inapparent; respiratory condition detected only by serological test. Occasionally severe with fever and chronic cough.

Special precautions– Histoplasmin skin test will detect sub-clinical infections in man. Chest X-rays will detect lung lesions.

Ringworm

Species involved – hedgehogs; rodents and a wide range of other mammals including bats. Occasionally birds.

Symptoms in animals – usually some hair loss around crusty lesions; may be localised to glabrous skin or to head or tail. Often very difficult to detect. In birds usually confined to unfeathered parts of body.

Sources of agent – spores on animal skins or contaminated material.

Route of infection – invades the skin.

Resistance – may persist many months in dried state. Rather resistant to chemical and physical agents. Destroyed by sunlight.

Symptoms in man – localised circular inflamed areas. Pruritis. Lesions usually on hands or face.

Special precautions – some fungi can be detected by their ability to fluoresce under ultraviolet light.

RICKETTSIAL DISEASES

This group of diseases is transmitted by arthropods, either by bites or by infected arthropod faeces. The group includes the very important typhus and spotted fevers; however, the agents, with the exception of Q fever, die very rapidly outside the arthropod vectors and are therefore only dangerous to people in contact with infected live arthropods. The exception, Q fever, is considered below.

Q fever

Species involved – widespread in small mammals (e.g. rodents, bandicoots) also in birds.

Symptoms in animals – usually symptomless.

Sources of agent – transmitted by ticks and lice. Shed in arthropod faeces.

Route of infection – aerosol from arthropod faeces. Occasionally arthropod bite.

Resistance – highly resistant to chemical and physical agents, including desiccation. Survives long periods in dried faeces or tissues of ticks, especially if frozen. Survives up to twenty-four hours in 0.5 per cent formalin.

Symptoms in man – influenza-like, sudden onset of headache, fever, sometimes pneumonia.

Special precautions – vaccination can be carried out and confers good protection.

NON-SPECIFIC CONDITION

Hypersensitivity

Species involved – may be any species.

Symptoms in animals – none.

Sources of agent – hair, fur, hide or feather dust, faecal material.

Route of infection – usually inhalation, may be contact.

Resistance – not applicable. Allergic factors will be present continually.

Symptoms in man – urticaria, hay fever, asthma, running eyes. 'Bird Fancier's Lung' – chronic cough, constant exposure will aggravate the condition.

Special precautions – only affects certain hypersensitive individuals; sensitivity in these people is usually highly specific. Ventilation and face masks will reduce incidence. Employ allergic personnel away from source.

151

Appendix 3

Check-list of Eye Sizes and Colours for Birds and Mammals

BRITISH, EUROPEAN AND NORTH AMERICAN BIRDS

Gaviidae

Black-throated diver N.Am. Pacific loon
Gavia arctica
Adult   12 mm   red
Juv.   12 mm   brown

Great northern diver N.Am. common loon
Gavia immer
Adult   14 mm   red
Juv.   14 mm   dark brown

White-billed diver N.Am. yellow-billed loon
Gavia adamsii
Adult   14 mm   red
Juv.   14 mm   dark brown

Red-throated diver N.Am. red-throated loon
Gavia stellata
Adult   11 mm   red/brown
Juv.   11 mm   brown

Podicipedidae

Great crested grebe   *Podiceps cristatus*
Adult   8 mm   carmine red/narrow
                    orange inner ring
Juv.   8 mm   orange/inner ring pale
                    yellow

Red-necked grebe   N.Am. Holboell's grebe
Podiceps griseigena
Adult   7.5 mm   dark brown
Juv.   7.5 mm   yellowish-brown

Slavonian grebe   *Podiceps auritus*
Adult   7 mm   orange/pink – silvery
                    inner ring around
                    pupil

Black-necked grebe   N.Am. eared grebe
Podiceps nigricollis
Adult   7 mm   orange/pink – silvery
                    inner ring around
                    pupil
Juv.   7 mm   paler

Little grebe   *Podiceps ruficollis*
Adult   5 mm   red/brown
Juv.   5 mm   light brown

Procellariidae – Tubinares

Leach's petrel   *Oceanodroma leucorrhoa*
Adult   5 mm   dark brown

Storm petrel   *Hydrobates pelagicus*
Adult   4 mm   dark brown

Manx shearwater   *Puffinus puffinus*
Adult   8 mm   dark brown

Sooty shearwater   *Puffinus griseus*
Adult   9 mm   dark brown

Fulmar   *Fulmarus glacialis*
Adult   11 mm   dark brown

Sulidae

Gannet   *Sula bassana*
Adult   12 mm   Pale grey, nearly white,
                    with fine black outer
                    ring
Juv.   12 mm   greyish-blue
Fledgling 12 mm   dark brown

Phalacrocoracidae

Cormorant   N.Am. great cormorant
Phalacrocorax carbo
Adult   11 mm   dark green
Juv.   11 mm   brown

Shag   *Phalacrocorax aristotelis*
Adult   10 mm   dark green
Juv.   10 mm   greyish-brown

Ardeidae

Heron   *Ardea cinerea*
Adult   13 mm   citron
Juv.   13 mm   cream

Purple heron   *Ardea purpurea*
Adult   12 mm   orange
Juv.   12 mm   yellow

Little egret   *Egretta garzetta*
Adult   8 mm   citron yellow
Juv.   8 mm   pale yellow

Squacco heron   *Ardeola ralloides*
Adult   7 mm   golden yellow
Juv.   7 mm   pale yellow

Night heron   *Nycticorax nycticorax*
Adult   12 mm   carmine red
Juv.   12 mm   golden yellow
Immat.   12 mm   red

Little bittern   *Ixobrychus minutus*
Adult♂   6 mm   golden yellow
Adult♀   6 mm   citron yellow
Juv.   6 mm   greenish-yellow

Bittern   *Botaurus stellaris*
Adult   11-12 mm   golden yellow
Juv.   11-12 mm   pale yellow

American bittern   *Botaurus lentiginosus*
Adult   10-11 mm   yellow

Threskiornithidae

Spoonbill   *Platalia leucorodia*
Adult   10 mm   red
Juv.   10 mm   rust brown

Phoenicopteridae

Greater flamingo   *Phoenicopterus ruber*
Adult   8 mm   citron yellow
Juv.   8 mm   pale grey

Anatidae

Mallard   N.Am. common mallard
  Anas platyrhynchos
Adult♂   8 mm   dark brown
Adult♀   8 mm   light brown
Juv.   8 mm   grey-brown

Teal   *Anas crecca*
Adult   6 mm   dark brown
Juv.   6 mm   grey-brown

Garganey   *Anas querquedula*
Adult   6 mm   mid-brown
Juv.   6 mm   grey-brown

Gadwall   *Anas strepera*
Adult   8 mm   dark brown
Juv.   8 mm   grey-brown

Wigeon   *Anas penelope*
Adult   8 mm   mid-brown

Pintail   *Anas acuta*
Adult   8 mm   dark brown

Shoveler   *Spatula clypeata*
Adult♂   8 mm   citron yellow
Adult♀   8 mm   mid-brown
Juv.♂   8 mm   greyish-yellow

Juv. ♀   8 mm   greyish-brown

Mandarin   *Aix galericulata* (introduced)
Adult   7 mm   reddish-brown

Red-crested pochard   *Netta rufina*
Adult♂   9 mm   orange/red
Adult♀   9 mm   dark yellow
Juv.   9 mm   yellowish-brown

Scaup   *Aythya marila*
Adult♂   8 mm   citron yellow
Adult♀   8 mm   paler yellow
Juv.   8 mm   olive brown

Tufted duck   *Aytha fuligula*
Adult♂   8 mm   citron yellow
Adult♀   8 mm   dull yellow
Juv.♂   8 mm   brighter yellow than ♀

Pochard   *Aythya ferina*
Adult♂   9 mm   reddish-yellow in spring
Adult♂   9 mm   brilliant red-brown in
                    summer
Adult♀   9 mm   brown, beccoming
                    reddish hazel-brown
                    in summer
Juv.   9 mm   dark brown

Goldeneye   *Bucephala clangula*
Adult♂   9 mm   citron yellow
Adult♀   9 mm   dull yellow
Juv.♂   9 mm   citron yellow
Juv.♀   9 mm   dull yellow

Barrow's goldeneye   *Bucephala islandica*
Adult♂   9 mm   light yellow
Adult♀   9 mm   greenish-yellow

Long-tailed duck   N.Am. old squaw
  Clangula hyemalis
Adult♂   8 mm   reddish-yellow
Adult♀   8 mm   yellowish-brown
Juv.   8 mm   brownish-grey

Harlequin duck   *Histrionicus histrionicus*
Adult♂   9 mm   reddish-brown
Adult♀   9 mm   brown
Juv.   9 mm   brown

Velvet scoter   N.Am. white-winged scoter
  Melanitta fusca
Adult♂   9 mm   pearl white
Adult♀   9 mm   dark brown
Juv.   9 mm   brown

Surf scoter   *Melanitta perspicillata*
Adult♂   9 mm   white
Adult♀   9 mm   brown
Juv.   9 mm   greyish-brown

Common scoter   *Melanitta nigra*
Adult   8 mm   dark brown

Steller's eider   *Polysticta stelleri*

Taxidermy

Adult	8 mm	dark brown
Juv.	8 mm	greyish-brown

Eider *Somateria mollisima*

Adult ♂	10 mm	dark brown
Adult ♀	10 mm	yellowish-brown
Juv.	10 mm	greyish-brown

Red-breasted merganser *Mergus serrator*

Adult	9 mm	yellowish-brown

Goosander *Mergus merganser*

Adult ♂	10 mm	reddish-brown
Adult ♀	10 mm	brown
Juv.	10 mm	greyish-brown

Smew *Mergus albellus*

Adult ♂	8 mm	reddish-brown
Adult ♀	8 mm	brown

Males of mature age (3 years plus)
have pearl-grey eyes

Shelduck *Tadorna tadorna*

Adult ♂	9 mm	dark reddish-brown
Adult ♀	9 mm	brown
Juv.	9 mm	greyish-brown

Grey-lag goose *Anser anser*

Adult	12 mm	brown
Juv.	12 mm	brownish-grey

White-fronted goose *Anser albifrons*

Adult	11 mm	dark brown

Lesser white-fronted goose *Anser erythropus*

Adult	9 mm	dark brown

Bean goose *Anser fabalis*

Adult	11 mm	dark brown

Pink-footed goose
Anser brachyrhynchus

Adult	10 mm	brown

Snow goose *Anser caerulescens*

Adult	10-11 mm	dark brown

Brent goose *Branta bernicla*

Adult	8-9 mm	dark brown

Barnacle goose *Branta leucopsis*

Adult	10 mm	blackish-brown

Canada goose *Branta canadensis*

Adult	11-12 mm	greyish-brown

Red-breasted goose *Branta ruficollis*

Adult	8-9 mm	dark brown

Mute swan *Cygnus olor*

Adult ♂	12 mm	dark brown
Adult ♀	11 mm	dark brown

Whooper swan *Cygnus cygnus*

Adult ♂	12 mm	dark brown
Adult ♀	11 mm	dark brown

Bewick's swan *Cygnus bewickii*

Adult	10 mm	brown

Falconidae

Golden eagle *Aquila chrysaetos*

Adult ♂	18 mm	golden-yellow/brown
Adult ♀	18-19 mm	yellowish-brown
Juv.	18 mm	brownish-yellow

Spotted eagle *Aquila clanga*

Adult	13-14 mm	light brown to mid-brown
Juv.	13-14 mm	brownish-yellow

Lesser spotted eagle *Aquila pomarina*

Adult	13 mm	brown
Juv.	13 mm	brown

Buzzard *Buteo buteo*

Adult	12-13 mm	dark brown – varies from specimen to specimen

Rough-legged buzzard N.Am. rough-legged hawk *Buteo lagopus*

Adult	13-14 mm	ochre brown

Sparrowhawk *Accipiter nisus*

Adult ♂	8 mm	citron yellow changing to orange with age
Adult ♀	9 mm	citron yellow changing to orange with age
Juv.	8 mm	pale greenish-grey gradually becoming yellow

Goshawk *Accipiter gentilis*

Adult ♂	12 mm	golden yellow – changing to red-orange
Adult ♀	13-14 mm	yellow changing to orange
Juv.	12 mm	pale greenish-grey becoming yellow-orange

Red kite *Milvus milvus*

Adult	12-13 mm	yellowish-white turning silvery
Juv.	12-13 mm	greyish-white

Black kite *Milvus migrans*

Adult	12 mm	greyish-brown
Juv.	12 mm	dark brown

White-tailed eagle N.Am. gray sea eagle *Haliaeetus albicilla*

Adult ♂	17 mm	greyish-brown
Adult ♀	18 mm	greyish-brown
Juv.	17 mm	brown

Honey buzzard *Pernis apivorus*

Adult ♂	12 mm	golden yellow
Adult ♀	13 mm	citron yellow
Juv.	12 mm	brownish

Marsh harrier *Circus aeruginosus*

Adult ♂	10 mm	citron yellow

Adult ♀	11 mm	brownish-yellow
Juv.	10 mm	mid-brown

Hen harrier *Circus cyaneus*

Adult ♂	9 mm	golden yellow
Adult ♀	10 mm	yellow
Juv.	9 mm	whitish-grey to yellow

Montagu's harrier *Circus pygargus*

Adult ♂	9 mm	golden yellow
Adult ♀	10 mm	pale yellow
Juv.	9 mm	brown

Osprey *Pandion haliaetus*

Adult ♂	13 mm	citron yellow
Adult ♀	14 mm	citron yellow
Juv.	13 mm	golden yellow

Hobby *Falco subbuteo*

Adult ♂	9 mm	dark brown
Adult ♀	9 mm	dark brown

Peregine N.Am. duck hawk
Falco peregrinus

Adult ♂	11 mm	dark brown
Adult ♀	12 mm	dark brown

Lanner falcon *Falco biarmicus*

Adult ♂	12 mm	dark brown
Adult ♀	12 mm	dark brown

Saker falcon *Falco cherrug*

Adult ♂	11 mm	dark brown
Adult ♀	12 mm	dark brown
Juv.	11 mm	brown

Gyr falcon *Falco rusticolus*

Adult ♂	14 mm	dark brown
Adult ♀	15 mm	dark brown

Merlin *Falco columbarius*

Adult ♂	7 mm	dark brown
Adult ♀	8 mm	dark brown

Kestrel *Falco tinnunculus*

Adult	8 mm	dark brown

Tetraonidae

Red grouse *Lagopus scoticus*

Adult ♂	9 mm	dark brown

Ptarmigan N.Am. rock ptarmigan
Lagopus mutus

Adult	8 mm	dark brown

Black grouse *Lyrurus tetrix*

Adult ♂	10 mm	dark brown
Adult ♀	9 mm	dark brown

Capercaillie *Tetro urogallus*

Adult ♂	12 mm	brown
Adult ♀	10–11 mm	brown

Phasianidae

Red-legged partridge *Alectoris rufa*

Adult ♂	7 mm	light reddish-brown
Adult ♀	7 mm	light reddish-brown
Juv.	7 mm	brown

Common partridge N. Am. Hungarian partridge *Perdix perdix*

Adult	7 mm	mid-brown

Quail *Coturnix coturnix*

Adult	5 mm	reddish-brown
Juv.	5 mm	light brown

Pheasant *Phasianus colchicus*

Adult ♂	9 mm	ochre yellow
Adult ♀	8 mm	brown

(Eye colour can vary from specimen to specimen)

Rallidae

Water rail *Rallus aquaticus*

Adult ♂	6 mm	bright red
Adult ♀	6 mm	reddish-brown
Juv.	6 mm	greyish-green

Spotted crake *Porzana porzana*

Adult	5 mm	brown
Juv.	5 mm	greyish-brown

Baillon's crake *Porzana pusilla*

Adult	4 mm	dark red
Juv.	4 mm	light brown

Little crake *Porzana parva*

Adult	4.5 mm	dark red
Juv.	4.5 mm	light brown

Corncrake *Crex crex*

Adult	6 mm	ochre yellow
Juv.	6 mm	brown

Moorhen N.Am. Florida gallinule
Gallinula chloropus

Adult	6 mm	dark red
Juv.	6 mm	greyish-brown

Coot *Fulica atra*

Adult	7 mm	dark red
Juv.	7 mm	mid-brown

Haematopodidae

Oyster catcher *Haematopus ostralegus*

Adult	9 mm	vermilion
Juv.	9 mm	greyish-brown – 1st winter: yellowish-orange

Charadriidae

Lapwing *Vanellus vanellus*

Adult	9 mm	dark brown

Taxidermy

Ringed plover   *Charadrius hiaticula*
Adult   6.5 mm   dark brown

Little ringed plover   *Charadrius dubius*
Adult   5.5 mm   dark brown

Kentish plover   N. Am. snowy plover
   Charadrius alexandrinus
Adult   6 mm   dark brown

Grey plover   N.Am. black-bellied plover
   Pluvialis aquatarola
Adult   8 mm   dark brown

Golden plover   *Pluvialis apricaria*
Adult   8 mm   dark brown

Dotterel   *Eudromias morinellus*
Adult   8 mm   dark brown

Turnstone   *Arenaria interpres*
Adult   6.5 mm   dark brown
Juv.   6.5 mm   greyish-brown

Scolpacidae

Common snipe   N.Am. Wilson's snipe
   Gallinago gallinago
Adult   6 mm   dark brown

Great snipe   *Gallinago media*
Adult   6.5 mm   dark brown

Jack snipe   *Lymnocryptes minimus*
Adult   5 mm   dark brown

Woodcock   N.Am. American woodcock
   Scolopax rusticola
Adult   10mm   dark brown

Curlew   *Numenius arquata*
Adult   9 mm   dark brown

Whimbrel   *Numenius phaeopus*
Adult   8.5 mm   dark brown

Black-tailed godwit   *Limosa limosa*
Adult   7 mm   dark brown
Juv.   7 mm   greyish-brown

Bar-tailed godwit   *Limosa lapponica*
Adult   6.5 mm   dark brown

Green sandpiper   *Tringa ochropus*
Adult   5.5 mm   dark brown

Wood sandpiper   *Tringa glareola*
Adult   5.5 mm   dark brown

Redshank   *Tringa totanus*
Adult   6.5 mm   dark brown
Juv.   6.5 mm   greyish-brown

Spotted redshank   *Tinga erythropus*
Adult   6.5 mm   dark brown

Greenshank   *Tringa nebularia*
Adult   7 mm   dark brown
Juv.   7 mm   greyish-brown

Common sandpiper   *Tringa hypoleucos*
Adult   5 mm   dark brown

Terek sandpiper   *Tringa terek*
Adult   5.5 mm   dark brown

Dowitcher   N.Am. eastern dowitcher
   Limnodromus griseus
Adult   7 mm   dark brown

Knot   *Calidris canutus*
Adult   6 mm   dark brown
Juv.   6 mm   greyish-brown

Purple sandpiper   *Calidris maritima*
Adult   5.5 mm   dark brown

Little stint   *Calidris minuta*
Adult   4 mm   dark brown

Dunlin   N.A. Red-backed sandpiper
   Calidris alpina
Adult   4.5 mm   dark brown

Curlew sandpiper   *Calidris ferruginea*
Adult   5 mm   dark brown

Sanderling   *Calidris alba*
Adult   5 mm   dark brown
Juv.   5 mm   greyish-brown

Ruff   *Philomachus pugnax*
Adult♂   7 mm   dark brown
Adult♀ (Reeve) 6 mm   dark brown

Recurvirostridae

Avocet   *Recurvirostra avosetta*
Adult   7 mm   ochre to reddish-brown

Phalaropodidae

Grey phalarope   N.Am. red phalarope
   Phalaropus fulicarius
Adult   4.5 mm   dark brown

Red-necked phalarope   N.Am northern
   phalarope   *Phalaropus lobatus*
Adult   4 mm   dark brown

Burhinidae

Stone curlew   *Burhinus oedicnemus*
Adult   12 mm   pale yellow
Juv.   12 mm   yellowish-white

Glareolidae

Pratincole   *Glareola pratincola*
Adult   7 mm   dark brown

Cream-coloured courser   *Cursorius cursor*
Adult   7 mm   dark brown

Stercorariidae

Arctic skua   N.Am. arctic jaeger
Stercorarius parasiticus
Adult   8 mm   dark brown

Great skua   N.Am. skua   *Stercorarius skua*
Adult   10mm   dark brown

Pomarine skua   N.Am. pomarine jaeger
Stercorarius pomarinus
Adult   9 mm   dark brown

Long-tailed skua   N.Am. long-tailed jaeger
Stercorarius longicaudus
Adult   7-8 mm   dark brown

Laridae

Great black-backed gull   *Laurus marinus*
Adult   12 mm   ochre
Juv.   12 mm   greyish-brown

Lesser black-backed gull   *Larus fuscus*
Adult   11 mm   greyish-white to
                                      pale cream
Juv.   11 mm   greyish-brown

Herring gull   *Larus argentatus*
Adult   11 mm   yellowish-grey white

Common gull   *Larus canus*
Adult   10 mm   dark brown
Juv.   10 mm   greyish-brown

Glaucous gull   *Larus hyperboreus*
Adult   12 mm   bright yellow

Iceland gull   *Larus glaucoides*
Adult   11 mm   yellow
Juv.   11 mm   greyish-brown

Black-headed gull   *Larus ridibundus*
Adult   8 mm   reddish-brown
Juv.   8 mm   light brown

Sabine's gull   *Xema sabini*
Adult   7 mm   light brown

Kittiwake   *Rissa tridactyla*
Adult   8 mm   dark brown

Black tern   *Chlidonias niger*
Adult   5 mm   dark brown

Gull-billed tern   *Gelochelidon nilotica*
Adult   7.5 mm   dark brown

Common tern   *Sterna hirundo*
Adult   7 mm   dark brown

Arctic tern   *Sterna macrura*
Adult   7 mm   dark brown

Roseate tern   *Sterna dougallii*
Adult   6 mm   dark brown

Sooty tern   *Sterna fuscata*
Adult   7 mm   reddish-brown

Little tern   N.Am. least tern   *Sterna albifrons*
Adult   5 mm   blackish-brown
Juv.   5 mm   light brown

Sandwich tern   N.Am. Cabot's tern
Sterna sandvicensis
Adult   8 mm   dark brown

Alcidae

Razorbill   N.Am. razor-billed auk
Alca torda
Adult   9-10 mm   dark brown

Little auk   N.Am. dovekie   *Plautus alle*
Adult   6 mm   blackish-brown

Guillemot   N.Am. common murre
Uria aalge
Adult   10 mm   brown
Juv.   10 mm   greyish-brown

**Brunnich's guillemot   N.Am. Brunnich's
murre   *Uria lomvia***
Adult   10 mm   dark brown

Black guillemot   *Cepphus grylle*
Adult   7 mm   brown
Juv.   7 mm   greyish-brown

Puffin   *Fratercula arctica*
Adult   7 mm   pearl-white
Immat.   7 mm   brownish-grey

Columbidae

Stock dove   *Columba oenas*
Adult   8 mm   dark brown
Juv.   8 mm   greyish brown

Rock dove   *Columbia livia*
Adult   8 mm   orange-red/yellow
                                      inner ring
Juv.   8 mm   yellowish-brown

Wood pigeon   *Columba palumbus*
Adult   9 mm   pale beige
Juv.   9 mm   whitish-grey

Turtle dove   *Streptopelia turtur*
Adult   6 mm   yellow with red ring
                                      around pupil
Juv.   6 mm   brownish

Collared turtle dove   *Streptopelia decaocto*
Adult   6 mm   cherry-red
Juv.   6 mm   brownish

Cuculidae

Cuckoo   *Cuculus canorus*
Adult♂   7 mm   yellow
Adult♀   7 mm   ochre-yellow
Juv.   7 mm   greyish-brown

Strigidae

Barn owl   *Tyto alba*
Adult   11 mm   blackish-brown

Scops owl   *Otus scops*
Adult   8.5 mm   reddish-yellow
Juv.   8.5 mm   yellow

Eagle owl   *Bubo bubo*
Adult   23-24 mm   fire-orange

Snowy owl   *Nyctea scandiaca*
Adult   19-20 mm   citron yellow

Hawk owl   *Surnia ulula*
Adult   12-13 mm   citron yellow
Juv.   12-13 mm   bluish-yellow

Pygmy owl   *Glaucidium passerinum*
Adult   6-7 mm   bright citron yellow

Little owl   *Athene noctua*
Adult   10mm   citron yellow
Juv.   10 mm   whitish-yellow

Tawny owl   *Strix aluco*
Adult   16-17 mm   blackish-brown

Long-eared owl   *Asio otus*
Adult   11 mm   bright golden orange
Juv.   11 mm   pale yellow

Short-eared owl   *Asio flammeus*
Adult   11 mm   citron yellow
Juv.   11 mm   pale yellow

Tengmalm's owl   *Aegolius funereus*
Adult   10-11 mm   citron yellow
Juv.   10-11 mm   pale citron yellow

Caprimulgidae

Nightjar   *Caprimulgus europaeus*
Adult   9 mm   dark brown with
                           bluish-black pupil

Apodidae

Swift   *Apus apus*
Adult   6 mm   blackish-brown

Alcedinidae

Kingfisher   *Alcedo atthis*
Adult   6 mm   dark brown

Upupidae

Hoopoe   *Upupa epops*
Adult   5 mm   brown

Picidae

Green woodpecker   *Picus viridis*
Adult   8 mm   white
Juv.   8 mm   greyish-white

Great spotted woodpecker   *Dendrocopos major*
Adult   6 mm   brown to cherry-red
Juv.   6 mm   brown

Lesser spotted woodpecker   *Dendrocopos minor*
Adult   4 mm   carmine red

Wryneck   *Jynx torquilla*
Adult   5 mm   light brown
Juv.   5 mm   greyish-brown

Alaudidae

Crested lark   *Galerida cristata*
Adult   4.5 m   light brown

Thekla lark   *Galerida theklae*
Adult   4 mm   brown

Wood lark   *Lullula arborea*
Adult   4 mm   light brown

Sky lark   *Alauda arvensis*
Adult   4 mm   brown

Shore lark   N.Am. horned lark
    Eremophila alpestris
Adult   4.5 mm   dark brown

Hirundinidae

Swallow   *Hirundo rustica*
Adult   4 mm   dark brown

House martin   *Delichon urbica*
Adult   4 mm   dark brown

Sand martin   N. Am. bank swallow
    Riparia riparia
Adult   3.5 mm   dark brown

Oriolidae

Golden oriole   *Oriolus oriolus*
Adult ♂   6.5 mm   light purple/crimson
Adult ♀   6.5 mm   brown
Juv.   6.5 mm   brown

Corvidae

Raven   *Corvus corax*
Adult   12 mm   blackish-brown
Juv.   12 mm   greyish-brown

Carrion crow   *Corvus (corone) corone*
Adult   9 mm   dark brown

Hooded crow   *Corvus (corone) cornix*
Adult   9 mm   dark brown

Rook   *Corvus frugilegus*
Adult   9 mm   blackish-brown

Jackdaw   *Coloeus monedula*
Adult   7.5 mm   white
Juv.   7.5 mm   brown

Magpie   *Pica pica*
Adult   8 mm   dark brown

Jay   *Garrulus glandarius*
Adult   8 mm   bluish–white

Chough   *Pyrrhocorax pyrrhocorax*
Adult   7 mm   dark brown

Paridae

Great tit   *Parus major*
Adult   4 mm   blackish–brown

Blue tit   *Parus caeruleus*
Adult   3 mm   blackish–brown

Coal tit   *Parus ater*
Adult   3 mm   dark brown

Crested tit   *Parus cristatus*
Adult   3 mm   reddish–brown

Marsh tit   *Parus palustris*
Adult   3.5 mm   dark brown

Willow tit   N.Am. black–capped chickadee
   Parus montanus
Adult   3.5 mm   dark brown

Longtailed tit   *Aegithalos caudatus*
Adult   3 mm   dark brown

Bearded tit   *Panurus biarmicus*
Adult ♂   3.5 mm   chrome yellow
Adult ♀   3.5 mm   ochre yellow
Juv.   3.5 mm   pale yellow

Sittidae

Nuthatch   *Sitta europaea*
Adult   4.5 mm   mid–brown

Certhiidae

Tree creeper   N.Am. brown creeper
   Certhia familiaris
Adult   3 mm   dark brown

Troglodytidae

Wren   *Troglodytes troglodytes*
Adult   3 mm   dark brown

Cinclidae

Dipper   *Cinclus cinclus*
Adult   5.5 mm   light–brown

Turdidae

Mistle thrush   *Turdus viscivorus*
Adult   7 mm   dark brown

Fieldfare   *Turdus pilaris*
Adult   6.5 mm   dark brown

Song thrush   *Turdus philomelos*
Adult   6 mm   dark brown

Redwing   *Turdus musicus*
Adult   6 mm   dark brown

Ring ouzel   *Turdus torquatus*
Adult   6.5 mm   dark brown

Blackbird   *Turdus merula*
Adult   6.5 mm   dark brown

American robin   N.Am. robin
   Turdus migratorius
Adult   6.5 mm   dark brown

Wheatear   *Oenanthe oenanthe*
Adult   4.5 mm   dark brown
Juv.   4.5 mm   greyish–brown

Black wheatear   *Oenanthe leucura*
Adult   5.5 mm   brown

Stonechat   *Saxicola torquata*
Adult   4 mm   brown

Whinchat   *Saxicola rubetra*
Adult   4 mm   reddish–brown

Redstart   *Phoenicurus phoenicurus*
Adult   4.5 mm   dark brown

Black redstart   *Phoenicurus ochruros*
Adult   4.5 mm   dark brown

Nightingale   *Luscinia megarhynchos*
Adult   5 mm   mid–brown

Thrush nightingale   *Luscinia luscinia*
Adult   5 mm   dark brown

Bluethroat   *Lusconoa svecica*
Adult   4.5 mm   mid–brown

Robin   *Erithacus rubecula*
Adult   4.5 mm   blackish–brown

Sylviidae

Cetti's warbler   *Cettia cetti*
Adult   4.5 mm   mid–brown

Grasshopper warbler   *Locustella naevia*
Adult   4 mm   mid–brown

Reed warbler   *Acrocephalus scirpaceus*
Adult   4 mm   mid–brown

Sedge warbler   *Acrocephalus dumetorum*
Adult   4 mm   light brown

Melodious warbler   *Hippolais polyglotta*
Adult   4 mm   brown

Icterine warbler   *Hippolais icterina*
Adult   4 mm   dark brown

Olivaceous warbler   *Hippolais pallida*
Adult   3.5 mm   dark brown

Taxidermy

Blackcap   *Sylvia atricapilla*
Adult   4 mm   dark brown

Barred warbler   *Sylvia nisoria*
Adult♂   5 mm   bright yellow
Adult♀   5 mm   pale yellow
Juv.   5 mm   greyish–white

Garden warbler   *Sylvia borin*
Adult   5 mm   mid–brown

Whitethroat   *Sylvia communis*
Adult   4 mm   ochre–brown

Lesser whitethroat   *Sylvia curruca*
Adult   3.5 mm   light brown

Subalpine warbler   *Sylvia cantillans*
Adult   3.5 mm   reddish–brown

Dartford warbler   *Sylvia undata*
Adult   3.5 mm   reddish–orange

Fan–tailed warbler   *Cisticola juncidis*
Adult   3 mm   brown

Chiffchaff   *Phylloscopus collybita*
Adult   3.5 mm   dark brown

Willow warbler   *Phylloscopus trochilus*
Adult   3.5 mm   dark brown

Wood warbler   *Phylloscopus sibilatrix*
Adult   4 mm   dark brown

Regulidae

Goldcrest   *Regulus regulus*
Adult   3 mm   blackish–brown

Firecrest   *Regulus ignicapillus*
Adult   3 mm   brown

Muscicapidae

Spotted flycatcher   *Muscicapa striata*
Adult   4.5 mm   dark brown

Pied flycatcher   *Ficedula hypoleuca*
Adult   4.5 mm   brown

Prunellidae

Dunnock   *Prunella modularis*
Adult   4 mm   light brown

Motacillidae

Tree pipit   *Anthus trivialis*
Adult   4 mm   dark brown

Meadow pipit   *Anthus pratensis*
Adult   4 mm   dark brown

Rock pipit   *Anthus spinoletta*
Adult   4 mm   dark brown

White wagtail   *Motacilla alba*
Adult   4 mm   dark brown

Grey wagtail   *Motacilla cinerea*
Adult   4 mm   blackish–brown

Blue–headed wagtail   *Motacilla flava*
Adult   4 mm   dark brown

Bombycillidae

Waxwing   N.Am. Bohemian waxwing
   Bombycilla garrulus
Adult   6 mm   reddish–brown
Juv.   6 mm   brownish

Laniidae

Great grey shrike   N.Am. northern shrike
   Lanius excubitor
Adult   7 mm   dark brown

Lesser grey shrike   *Lanius minor*
Adult   6 mm   dark brown

Woodchat shrike   *Lanius senator*
Adult   5.5 mm   light brown

Red–backed shrike   *Lanius collurio*
Adult   5.5 mm   brown

Sturnidae

Starling   *Sturnus vulgaris*
Adult   5.5 mm   mid–brown

Spotless starling   *Sturnus unicolor*
Adult   5.5 mm   dark brown

Fringillidae

Hawfinch   *Coccothraustes coccothraustes*
Adult♂   5 mm   paleish–rose
Adult♀   5 mm   greyish–brown
Juv.   5 mm   greyish–white

Greenfinch   *Carduelis chloris*
Adult   4 mm   dark brown

Goldfinch   *Carduelis carduelis*
Adult   3.5 mm   dark brown

Siskin   *Carduelis spinus*
Adult   3 mm   dark brown

Linnet   *Carduelis cannabina*
Adult   3.5 mm   dark brown

Twite   *Carduelis flavirostris*
Adult   3.5 mm   dark brown

Redpoll   *Carduelis flammea*
Adult   3.5 mm   dark brown

Citril finch   *Carduelis citrinella*
Adult   3.5 mm   dark brown

Serin   *Serinus serinus*
Adult   3 mm   dark brown

MAMMALS

Bullfinch   *Pyrrhula pyrrhula*
Adult   4.5 mm   dark brown

Crossbill   N.Am. red crossbill
  Loxia curvirostra
Adult   4.5 mm   dark brown

Two-barred crossbill
  N.Am. white-winged crossbill
  Loxia leucoptera
Adult   4 mm   mid-brown

Chaffinch   *Fringilla coelebs*
Adult   4 mm   mid-brown

Brambling   *Fringilla montifringilla*
Adult   4 mm   blackish-brown

Yellowhammer   *Emberiza citrinella*
Adult   4.5 mm   dark brown

Corn bunting   *Emberiza calandra*
Adult   5 mm   dark brown

Cirl bunting   *Emberiza aureola*
Adult   4.5 mm   mid-brown

Rustic bunting   *Emberiza rustica*
Adult   4 mm   dark brown

Little bunting   *Emberiza pusilla*
Adult   3.5 mm   dark brown

Reed bunting   *Emberiza schoeniclus*
Adult   4 mm   blackish-brown

Snow bunting   *Plectrophenax nivalis*
Adult   4.5 mm   dark brown

Passeridae

House sparrow   *Passer (domesticus) domesticus*
Adult   4 mm   dark brown

Tree sparrow   *Passer montanus*
Adult   3.5 mm   mid-brown

When requiring eyes for the larger mammals it is always best to inform your supplier of the species that you require, the age of the animal and the sex. Here are some sizes and colours of the more common mammals' eyes that the preparator may wish to mount.

Specimen	Size	Colour
Badger	10 mm	dark brown
Bear, European brown	14–16 mm	dark brown
Bobcat	16–18 mm	mid-brown to yellow
Fallow deer	ask supplier	
Red deer	ask supplier	
Roe deer	ask supplier	
Fox	14–16 mm	Supplied with or without white corners
Lion, African	26–30 mm	ask supplier
Mink	8 mm	mid-brown
Muskrat	7 mm	dark brown
Otter	12 mm	dark brown
Porcupine, tree	10 mm	dark brown
Squirrel, grey	10–11 mm	dark brown
Squirrel, red	8–10 mm	dark brown
Wolf, timber	19–20 mm	ask supplier
Wolverine	13–14 mm	ask supplier

Appendix 4

Suppliers

USA

General

Jonas Brothers Inc., Taxidermist Suppliers, 1037 Broadway, Denver, Colorado, USA, supply all that the taxidermist will require, from bird and animal forms, tools and chemicals, teeth, jaws and tongues, to art supplies and instruction manuals

Artisan Supply Co., 4585 Harlands Drive, New Berlin, Wisconsin 53151

M. J. Hofmann Co., 963 Broadway, Brooklyn, New York 1121

Gosnell's Taxidermy & Supply, 24659 O'Neil Ave., Hayward, California 94544

Bob's Taxidermy Studios, 321 N. Perry Street, Johnstown, New York 12095

Tohickon Corporation, Rte 611, Ottsville, Pennsylvania 18942

Glass eyes

Robert J. Smith Glass Eyes, 14900 West 31st Street, Golden, Colorado 80401

J. W. Elwood Supply Co. Ltd, Box 3507, Omaha, Nebraska 68103

Van Dykes Taxidermy Supplies, Woonsocket, South Dakota 57385

ENGLAND AND EUROPE

General

Frank Joel Ltd, Museum Laboratory & Archaeological Supplies, The Manor House, Wareham, King's Lynn, Norfolk PE33 9AF, provides a wide variety of materials useful to the taxidermist, including adhesives, latex, Vinamould, silicone rubber, safety equipment, waxes, and dissection equipment.

Beeswax, paraffin wax, pearl glue

Fiddes & Son, Trade Street, Cardiff

Drysalters – dry colour, shellac a animal glue

George Hull, Lion House, 28 Horse Fair, Birmingham B1 1DF

Fat Liquor WWL

Sandoz, P.O. Box 4, Horsforth, Leeds LS18 4RP

Fibre-glass and resins, rubber latex, silicone rubber and polyurethane foam

The main office is: Strand Glassfibre, Brentway Trading Estate, Brentford, Middlesex. There are many branches of Strand Glassfibre in England. Write asking for the branch nearest to you.

Fibre-glass mattings

Fibre-glass Ltd, St Helens, Lancashire

Flock powders

Spraytex Manchester Ltd, 168–72 Oxford Road, Manchester 13

Filler Paste

Warwick Chemicals Ltd, 54 Willow Lane, Mitcham, Surrey

Fleximould

Messrs Dohn Ltd, 167 Victoria Street, London SW1

Glass eyes

Watkins & Doncaster, Fourthrows, Hawkhurst, Kent.

Otto Linderman, Hamburgh 1, Amsinckstrasse 4–8, West Germany

Karl Lange, Tierglausaugen, Postfach 22, 8621, Grub am Forst, West Germany

FA.TAC Bouten, Venlo Industrieterrein, Veegtes, Veegtestraat 13, Holland

Lankrolin

Watkins & Doncaster, Fourthrows, Hawkhurst, Kent

Needles

British Needle Co. Ltd, Edward Street, Redditch, Worcs. B97 6EX. Will also quote for special needles made to order

162

Negocoll

Obtainable through import licence (made in Switzerland) from Messrs Pytram Ltd, Pytram Works, Dunbar Road, New Malden, Surrey

Osteological cement

North Eastern Rubber Co. Ltd, P.O. Box 6, Cliver Street, North Shields, Tyne & Wear NE29 6YL. Boscolyn cement No. 5293 is particularly useful for osteological work being both quick-drying and transparent

Paralene CFT

Yorkshire Chemicals, Selby, Yorkshire

Plasters and impression compounds – Calspar Dental Plaster, Kaffir D Plaster

Zelgan, Claudius Ashe, 78 Mount Pleasant, Liverpool

Plastic putty

Eagle Works, Wednesbury, West Midlands, WS10 7LT

Polythene – bags, rolls, sheets

Transatlantic Plastics Ltd, Garden Estate, Ventnor, Isle of Wight PO38 1YJ

Polystyrene tubes

Henleys Medical Supplies Ltd, Alexandra Works, Clarendon Road, Hornsey Road, London N8 0DL. Supplies a range of small airtight tubes for storing small mammal and small bird skins

Polyurethane foam

Baxenden Chemicals Co., Bibby Chemicals Co., Paragon Works, Baxenden, Nr Accrington, Lancs. Supplies a self-skinning foam suitable for manikins. Ask for the leaflet 'Isocyanates and Resins, hazards and safe handling procedure'

Polyurethanes

Caradate 30: Shell Chemicals UK Ltd, Shell Centre, Downstream Building, London SE1

Bibbithane: Oleo Chemical Department, Bibby Chemicals, King Edward Street, Liverpool L3 7AD

P.V.C. Pastes

Vycoat (air-drying P.V.C.): Plastic Coatings Ltd, Industrial Estate, Winsford, Cheshire

Welvic paste: ICI, Temple Chambers, 33 Brazenose Street, Manchester

Resins

Membrano: Membrano Ltd, Harrogate, Yorkshire

Polyester resin: Trylon Ltd, Thrift Street, Wollaston, Northamptonshire

Belzona: Belzona Ltd, Harrogate, Yorkshire

Rubber compounds

Silicone rubber: Midland Silicones, 406-7 Royal Exchange, Manchester

Revultex compound (latex rubber): Bellman Ivey & Carter, 110a Mill Lane, West Hampstead, London NW6

Simplex Rapid

Howmedica International Ltd, Dental Fillings Division, 49 Grayling Road, London N16 0BT

Soaps and creams

Deb Chemical Proprietaries Ltd, Forfar Works, Belper, Derby DE5 1JX. Supplies anti-bacterial soaps and resin removal creams and wall mounting dispensers

Swan Morton scalpels

John Bell & Croydon, 54 Wigmore Street, London W1

Tow

Ross James & Buncle Ltd, 109 Restalrigg Road, Edinburgh 6

Vinalak, Vinamould

Messrs Vinyl Products Ltd, Butter Hill, Carshalton, Surrey

Wacker Silicon

Micro Products, 22 The Green, West Drayton, Middlesex

Waxes

A. F. Suter & Co. Ltd, 60 Dace Road, Bow, London E3 2NQ

Wood-wool – coarse and fine grades

Leicester Wood-wool Co., Nottingham Street, Leicester

Zelex and Zelgan

Amalgamated Dental Co. Ltd, Solila House, 7 Swallow Street, London W1

Index

accidents, 13
acetone, 15, 24, 25
ageing, 40-1
air-drying, 132-3
Akeley, K., 88, 89
alcohol, 15, 22, 43, 95
alum, 15, 19, 25, 27-8, 105
ammonium hydroxide, 125, 130, 131
amphibians, 117
anatomy, 33-5
animal glue, 14
antiformin, 126
antlers, 29
arsenic, 15, 26, 28-9
artificial body: bird, 51-2, 57-8, 61-2; mammal, 74-5, 80, 85-94
aspergillosis, 150

bacteria: cause of decay, 24; halophilic, 25; killing, 24-5; see also diseases
bacterial decay in mammal skins, 24
bats, skinning, 77
bead glue, see carpenter's glue
beeswax, 15, 31, 52, 95, 110, 135-7
beetles, cause of damage, 26
binding, 67-8
birds, 43-68; anatomy, 34; measuring, 37; mounting, 61-8; of prey, 141; protection of, 139-43; skinning, 43-60; tongues, 20
body fat, see fat
Booth, E.T., 132
borax, 15, 25, 26, 27, 30, 95, 100, 135
brine solution, 24
Browne, Montagu, 26-7, 100, 117
brucellosis, 146

camphor, 15, 26, 27, 28
Canada balsam, 15, 135, 136
capsicum powder, 15
carbolic acid (phenol), 15, 25, 27
carbon tetrachloride, 15, 22, 129, 130
carding fins, 101
care and maintenance of specimens, 17-18
carpenter's glue, 15
casting, 30-2; fish, 104-16
Castogel, 30
celluloid, 32

chalk, 26
Chapin, 26; stitch, 57, 68
chemicals used in taxidermy, 15-17
chloride of lime, 15, 26
chloroform, 30
clay, powdered, 23
cleaning: fur and feather, 22-3; skins, 49, 73
cleaning drum, 23
colour changes in skins, 25, 27, 28
contact casting in fibre-glass, 89
corrosive sublimate, 15
crec-o-pearl essence, 102-3, 116
crustaceans, 119

Davie, O., 27
degreasing agents, 25, 78, 129, 130-1
desiccative powder, 133
dextrin, powdered, 15
diseases: bacterial, 146-7; fungal, 149-50; precautions against, 12-13, 124, 146-51; rickettsial, 150; viral, 149
drysalters, 162
dyeing grasses, 134-5
dyes, multi-purpose, 135

embalming, 9
enzymes, 125
eyes: artificial, for fish, 115; positioning, 66, 84; sizes, 152-61; suppliers, 162

fat, removing, 43, 48-9, 74
fat liquor, 15, 79
feather tracts, 43, 68
fibre-glass, 89-90, 92, 95, 111-14, 162
fixing, 24-5
fleshing board, 74
flexible moulds, 30
Fleximould, 30, 162
flock powders, 15, 162
flour, 28
foliage, preserving, 132-4
formaldehyde (formalin), 16, 27, 29, 101, 119
formic acid, 78, 79
freeze-drying, 120-3; drying times, 121; initial freezing, 122
frogs, 118
fuller's earth, 16, 23
fungal diseases, see diseases